OXFORD
UNIVERSITY PRESS

World of Science

Graham Booth
Bob McDuell
John Sears

OXFORD
UNIVERSITY PRESS

Great Clarendon Street, Oxford OX2 6DP

Oxford University Press is a department
of the University of Oxford. It furthers the
University's objective of excellence in research,
scholarship, and education by publishing
worldwide in

Oxford New York

*Athens Auckland Bangkok Bogotá
Buenos Aires Calcutta Cape Town
Chennai Dar es Salaam Delhi Florence
Hong Kong Istanbul Karachi Kuala
Lumpur Madrid Melbourne Mexico City
Mumbai Nairobi Paris Sao Paulo
Singapore Taipei Tokyo Toronto Warsaw
with associated companies in Berlin Ibadan*

Oxford is a registered trade mark of Oxford
University Press

British Library Cataloguing in Publication Data
Data available

ISBN 0 19 914699 3

Acknowledgements

*The publisher would to thank the following for their kind permission to reproduce the
following photographs:*

p 6 Mary Evans Picture Library, Robert Harding Picture Library (bottom), p 8 Science Photo
Library/Maximillian Stock Ltd, p 9 Oxford Scientific Films/ S Turner (top), OSF/A & S Carey
(centre), SPL/Dr P Marazzi (bottom), p 10 OSF/A Root (top), Robert Harding (bottom), p 11
OSF/J McCammon (top), OSF/G Bernard (centre), OSF/A & S Carey (right & bottom), p 13
Allsport/B Martin (bottom), p 14 OSF/M Fogden (top), Anthony Blake (centre & bottom), p 17
Robert Harding, p 18 SPL/K Eward (top), OSF/G Cox (bottom), p 20 SPL/Biophoto Associates,
pp 31, 37 J Allan Cash, p 39 Colorsport, p 40 Allsport, p 42 J Allan Cash, Allsport (bottom), p
43 Tony Stone/N Dolding, p 46 Format Photographers, p 48 J Allan Cash, p 50 SPL/F Leroy,
OSF/D Dennis (right), J Allan Cash (bottom left), p 51 SPL, p 53 OSF, p 54 SPL/Professor P
Motta, p 56 Format/L Woolett, p 58 SPL/ Science Pictures Ltd (left), OSF/S Camazine, p 59
SPL/M Meadows, p 60 SPL/J Berger, Max-Planck Institute, p 62 J Allan Cash, p 64 Mary Evnas
(top), Format/R Peters, p 69 SPL/A Syred, p 70 J Allan Cash, p 79 SPL/W & D McIntyre, p
81 J Allan Cash (top), SPL/H Morgan (centre), p 85 SPL/A Bartel, p 91 OSF/P Parks, OSF/A
Macewen, J Allan Cash (bottom), SPL, p 92 OSF/London Scientific Films, p 93 OSF/G Bernard
(left), SPL/Professor P Motta (right), OSF/London Scientific Films (top), p 94 OSF, OSF/B Watts
(right), p 95 OSF/D Fleetham, OSF/K Gowlett, OSF/D Fleetham, J Allan Cash (bottom right),
Image Bank (top), p 96 J Allan Cash, p 98 OSF/P Franklin (left), OSF/N Benrie (right), OSF/S
Osolinski (bottom), p 99 J Allan Cash, p 100 Corbis UK Ltd, p 102 OSF/J Dermid (left), J Allan
Cash (right), p 103 J Allan Cash, p 104 Dr A Waltham (right), GeoScience Features, pp 105,
106 J Allan Cash, p110,111 Image Bank, p 114 Holt Studios, p 115 OSF/D Bown, p 116
Anthony Blake

Additional photography by Peter Gould

The illustrations are by:
John Paul Early, Jane Fern, Nick Hawken, Ian Heard, Gillian Martin and Gecko Ltd

Cover Photographs: Manfred Kage/Oxford Scientific Films

Produced by Gecko Ltd, Bicester
Printed and bound by Mateu Cromo S.A., Spain

Introduction: Being a scientist

You will have a good idea of what science is from topics you have covered in primary school. You will continue to study science throughout your secondary school.

You know that science can be split into a number of subjects:

- **biology** is the study of living things, whether plants or animals
- **chemistry** is the study of matter and the way that changes or reactions can occur
- **physics** is the study of how matter behaves and the relationships between matter and energy.

There are other sciences including astronomy, geology, and meteorology. Your science course for Year 9 will cover all of these sciences in a broad and balanced way. In Years 10 and 11 you may continue to study science either as one subject or as a number of separate subjects.

Practical science

By now you will have done quite a lot of practical science. You will have planned experiments, carried them out, taken results and drawn conclusions. You will continue to do more experiments and apply good scientific methods to problems. These problems may be ones you have thought of or ones other people suggest to you.

The world of science

You are moving into a scientific world. You will continue to hear of new discoveries, inventions, and technologies; about genes, isotopes and microelectronics. Everybody needs to know the words scientists use. They need to have some understanding of important scientific issues, for example: the best use of energy resources, the effect of exhaust fumes on the environment, and the peaceful use of radioactivity.

Many people work in science or subjects that rely heavily on science and technology. You could well earn your living as a scientist. It is said that there are more scientists working today than ever before. It is certain in years to come science will continue to be a very important aspect of our lives.

We hope, as you use these books, you will learn the basic science you will need, and, more importantly, become enthusiastic about science.

Graham Booth
Bob McDuell
John Sears

Teacher's notes:
Chapter sections

Chapter sub-sections are denoted by line separators. Further details are given in the Teacher's Guide.

Summary pages

This book contains a series of Summary pages that revise the material covered in the books.

Self test

There are two Self tests (at Foundation/Higher levels) to help with preparation for examinations.

Questions at three levels

 = answerable from the page

 = needs some student interaction

 = requires student interaction

Contents

POPULATIONS AND PROCESSES

Pioneers in America (date) laying out bison skins to dry. The pile of bones in the background is waiting to be turned into fertilizer.

The seaweeds growing on this wreck provide food for fish and other aquatic life

As Dead as a Dodo

The dodo was a flightless bird that lived in Mauritius, an island in the Indian Ocean. When sailors landed on the island they killed so many dodos that the bird became extinct.

1. Explain how a change in climate could affect the number of individuals in a population.

2. Explain how a change in food supply could affect the number of individuals in a population.

3. Explain how the arctic lynx and snowshoe hare populations depend on each other.

Population change

The impact of people

A **population** is a group of organisms of the same species living in the same place. When Europeans first arrived in America, there were over 60 million bison there. As the settlers moved west, they killed bison to feed the men who built the railways. After about 15 years, only a handful of bison remained.

Natural changes to populations

Populations also change without any interference from people. What natural events might affect a population size?

The food supply obviously affects a population. If food is very scarce, some individuals will die of starvation. When there is plenty of food, insects and birds lay more eggs. This means the population grows rapidly to take advantage of the extra food. When there is less food, the adults lay fewer eggs and fewer young survive to breed.

A change in the space where the population lives will also affect the carrying capacity. A sunken ship provides extra places for seaweed to grow. This will increase the seaweed population. Where a river floods, grassland will be reduced and populations living on the grassland will fall.

Over a period of time, the climate may change. If the world is warming up, there will be less tundra. Populations living on the frozen land will fall. Local changes in climate can also affect population size. In a particularly warm year, more plants may grow. This in turn will support larger animal populations.

Predators and prey

If one animal eats another, their populations affect each other. The numbers of predators affect the population size of the prey they eat. The graph below shows the numbers of arctic lynx and snowshoe hares living in an area of Canada over a period of time. The lynx eats the hares. When the lynx population is large, the lynx eat so many hares that the hare population falls. The reduced supply of hares for food means the lynx population falls. This allows more hares to survive, and the cycle starts again.

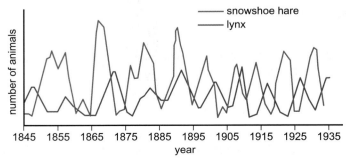

The lynx and snowshoe hare populations rise and fall in a regular alternating pattern.

Human population change

Like any species, the human population size also changes. This graph shows how the population has grown in England and Wales. There are three phases. First there was a gradual increase up to 1348. At this point the Black Death reached England and many people died. The second phase shows a recovery and levelling off up to about 1680. After this there is a dramatic rise in the third phase. This happened during the industrial and agricultural revolutions. Improved farming and technology meant people had more work and more food. People were healthier so the population grew.

Regions of the world

This rapid growth has happened in all parts of the world. The human population is rising very fast, though the rate of growth is different in different countries. Recently population growth has slowed down in the western world. The main growth in numbers is now in Africa and South America. The second graph shows how the population has grown in different regions of the world.

Young and old populations

Another way of studying human population patterns is to look at age graphs. The two below show different populations. In the first population, people live for a long time and have few children. The population is old. This is typical of a wealthier, more developed country where hygiene and health care are good. In the second one, few people live to be old but lots of babies are born. The population is young. This type of population is common in less wealthy developing countries. Health care is not widely available and food may be scarce so people do not live so long.

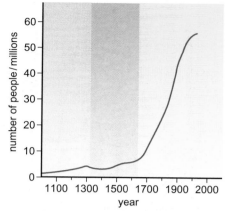

The human population growth in England and Wales

> ### Did You Know?
>
> The Black Death, or bubonic plague, spread from China to Europe in the fourteenth century. In 1348–9 over one-third of the people in England died of the plague.

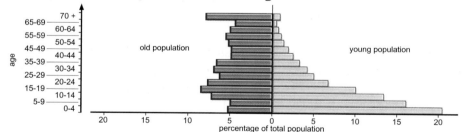

These graphs show the age profiles of two different populations

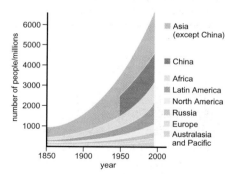

This graph shows how the population in the developed countries such as Europe and North America is growing more slowly than in developing countries such as Asia and Africa

1. Why did the industrial revolution allow such a rapid increase in population?

2. Why do you think that population growth is fastest in the poorest regions of the world?

3. Explain why a low birth rate could produce the kind of age distribution pattern seen on the left-hand age profile graph.

4. Are humans likely to become extinct?

> ### What Do You Think?
>
> If we could cure all diseases, what would control our population size?

Population growth

Thomas Malthus wrote about population growth as long ago as 1798. He saw that populations grow geometrically – they go up by multiples of 2. A single organism becomes 2, then 4, 8, 16, and so on. He thought the food supply could not keep up with this rapid increase in population. The food supply therefore limited the size of the population.

A typical population curve – bacteria

It is easiest to study population growth by looking at simple organisms such as bacteria. They can be grown in a fermenter. Bacteria are put into a nutrient solution in the fermenter and kept warm. They reproduce and the number of cells can be measured.

The graph shows how the population changes.

1 At first there is plenty of food and space and so the bacteria reproduce quickly. The population grows rapidly.
2 Gradually there is less food to go round and the bacteria do not reproduce so quickly. More of them die. The population becomes stable. The number of new bacteria is the same as the number of bacteria that die.
3 The population starts to decrease. This is because the food supply is being used up, and waste products from the bacteria are building up and poisoning them.
4 Eventually all the bacteria may die, and the population becomes extinct.

Populations in the real world

Populations do not normally live in closed containers! In the wild, populations have a more constant supply of food and their wastes are removed. The population reaches a balanced number where it remains stable. This number is called the **carrying capacity** of the environment. It is the number of organisms that can be supported by the ecosystem.

Most populations reach their carrying capacity after a rapid growth. This can be plotted as an S-shaped curve, like parts **1** and **2** of the graph. The death of a population is much less predictable as it may depend on many different factors.

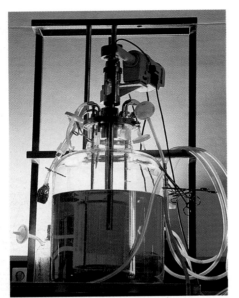

A fermenter is a large container used to grow a population of bacteria

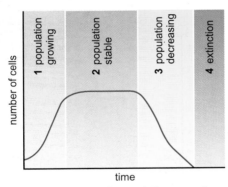

The main stages of population growth are shown on this typical population growth curve

1 Describe the shape of a typical population growth curve.

2 Calculate the number of bacteria that can be produced in 24 hours from one cell, if the cells divide every 30 minutes.

3 Make a graph of the bacteria in question **2** up to seven divisions. Put the number of cells (population size) on the vertical axis and the time on the horizontal axis.

4 What factors might affect the carrying capacity of a population of rabbits?

Even sheep are different

When you look around at your class everyone is different. A field of sheep might look all the same, but each one is different.

Variation – inherited and environmental

All living things are different in some ways. In biology we call these differences **variation**. There are two main things that cause individuals to vary.

The first is **inheritance** (genes). For example, panthers are black leopards. They have genes that make their coats black. Other leopards have genes for spotted coats. We call this **inherited variation**.

The second cause of variation is through things that happen during the organism's life. If you had a cut it might leave a scar. This would make you different from most other people. This is **environmental variation**.

Interaction between genes and environment

The cause of variation is usually more complex than these simple examples. The way we look cannot usually be described simply as inherited variation or environmental variation. Most variation is an **interaction** between the genes and the environment. Think about someone who has one blue eye and one brown eye. The genes for both eyes are the same. When the genes (instructions) were used to make the eye colour, something went a bit wrong in one of the eyes. Some of the enzymes that make the colour in one of the eyes may have been affected by a chemical from outside. Interactions are not only negative. Many genes are designed to be 'switched on' by chemicals from the environment.

Imagine making a whole person from one cell. The instructions need reading and interpreting. It is like having a recipe for curry. A small change in the recipe can make a big difference to the final taste. The curry turns out slightly different each time. In the same way, genes in slightly different environments create different effects. This is especially true for complex organisms with many genes.

Even cartoon sheep are different

The difference in coat colour is because of inherited variation

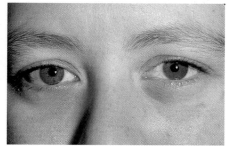
The colour difference in these eyes is caused by the environment

---

1 Explain the difference between inherited and environmental variation.

2 Identical twins have the same genes. We can tell them apart if we know them well. How have the differences between them come about?

3 Height depends on both genes and the environment.
Suggest how the environment might affect a person's height.

4 Why is the environment more likely to affect the appearance of a complex organism than a more simple one?

What Do You Think?

Is every fly you see different?

9

Natural selection

Have you ever wondered why we are not knee-deep in ants? Ants breed at an enormous rate. The queen ant produces thousands of eggs. When adults leave the nest as flying ants, they come out in great swarms. So why do we not see more and more ants everywhere? The answer is that most of them do not survive. This is also true for other organisms. Some plants produce millions of seeds; some animals produce millions of eggs. Most of the young never make it to adulthood. There is an over-production of young.

A struggle for existence

You may have seen film of turtles hatching. As they run down the beach to the sea, the baby turtles are attacked by flocks of gulls. Many are eaten. Once in the sea they have to escape from predators like sharks. Again many are eaten. Finally they have to survive long enough to find a mate and then make their way back to the beach to lay their eggs. There is a struggle for existence. This pattern is the same for all organisms. They are all competing to survive. Many die along the way.

If each female turtle manages to produce just two young which survive then the turtle population will stay the same over a period of time. In practice some turtles produce many young which survive, and others produce very few.

Natural selection

Individuals in a population are all different. Only some survive to breed, and only these survivors pass on their genes to the next generation. The ones that survive are usually those that are best suited to the conditions. Their genes are passed in large numbers to the next generation. It is *as if* nature has selected the best from the different individuals produced in each generation. The process is called **natural selection**. Of course, there is also an element of luck in the process. Even a well adapted organism might unluckily be killed in a flood.

Flying termites are produced in huge numbers, but they do not all survive

Young turtles make an easy meal for waiting predators

Did You Know?

Fish, insects, and many other animals produce large numbers of young and leave them to fend for themselves. Birds and mammals have smaller families but feed and look after their young. The young are more likely to survive.

1. Explain why we are not knee-deep in ants.

2. Why does each female turtle need to produce only two surviving young for the population to stay steady?

3. Explain how natural selection works.

4. Why would an accident to a well suited organism probably not affect the species in the long run?

Artificial selection

Natural selection and adaptation

Young turtles have to contend with the gulls waiting to catch them when they hatch. Gulls are only active during the day. If the turtles hatch at night, they have more chance of surviving. If a few of the turtles have a gene which makes them hatch at night, these turtles will have a better chance of getting to the sea. If they survive to breed, then they will probably pass this gene on. The next generation will have more turtles that hatch at night.

Eventually all the turtles will hatch at night. The turtles that hatch at night have been **selected** and become **adapted** to their environment. The turtle species has changed. This is **evolution**. The process of evolution depends on variation. The population has lots of different individuals. When the environment changes, some individuals will be suited to it. They will be selected.

Farmers have bred wheat over the centuries to improve the grain

Selective breeding

People did not know how this process worked centuries ago, but they had been selecting the best individuals to breed together. Early farmers sowed seed from plants that had produced a lot of seed. They bred their strongest bulls with the cows that had produced the most milk. These kinds of choices gradually produced new domestic varieties of crops and animals. This process is called **artificial selection**.

People have also used artificial selection to breed pets. All dogs, from Jack Russells to St Bernards, come from the same original species. All the 120 different breeds have been produced by selecting parents that have particular features and breeding them together. Jack Russells were bred for badger hunting. People chose dogs with strong jaws, aggressive natures, and short legs. Eventually they came up with a breed that produces similar dogs each generation. At this point the breed can be recognized as separate.

It is hard to believe these two animals are the same species

1. Explain how a turtle population could gradually change to hatch at night.

2. If you wanted to breed a pig which produced many young and had very thick skin, how would you go about it?

3. You might have to breed for many generations before succeeding in getting a variety you wanted. Why do you think this is?

4. Do you think it is right to breed plants and animals artificially to increase their yield?

What Do You Think?

If the only dogs were Chihuahuas and St Bernards, would they be separate species?

Energy and cells

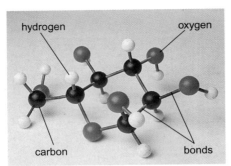

A glucose molecule contains carbon, hydrogen, and oxygen atoms held together by bonds

Living is an active process. All the processes of life use energy, so every cell in your body needs energy.

The main source of energy for animals is their food. The chemicals in food have very large molecules. When the organism breaks up these molecules energy is released which can be used to do other things (such as making the organism move).

Aerobic respiration

Cells break down glucose (a sugar) for their energy supply.

The way to break down fully the glucose uses oxygen from the air. Experiments using radioactive chemicals show us that glucose is fully broken down to carbon dioxide and water. The whole process is called **aerobic respiration**. It is summarized in the equation below.

glucose + oxygen → energy + carbon dioxide + water

Respiration happens in the mitochondria of all cells. It is an **oxidation** reaction. It happens in small steps with a bit of energy being released at each stage. The energy released is stored in a chemical called **ATP**. Every cell contains lots of ATP ready to use.
ATP drives all the chemical reactions that keep you alive.

Gas in the air	Amount in air we breathe in/%	Amount in air we breathe out/%
nitrogen	79	79
oxygen	20	16
carbon dioxide	0.03	4

We take in oxygen for aerobic respiration from the air we breathe in.
We get rid of carbon dioxide into the air we breathe out.

Plants and animals both make ATP by aerobic respiration. Plants also make ATP using the Sun's energy during photosynthesis.

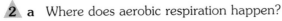

1 Why do living things need energy?

2 a Where does aerobic respiration happen?

   b Describe how aerobic respiration occurs.

3 Look at the table. Compare the percentages in the air breathed in and the air breathed out for
   a oxygen b carbon dioxide.

4 a How do plants get most of their energy during daylight?

   b Why would this be different at night?

Anaerobic respiration

Living in the mud

Most living things use oxygen to release energy from food by respiration. But some organisms live in places where there is very little oxygen. In the thick mud at the bottom of a pond there is very little oxygen. Some bacteria live in this mud. They can break down glucose without using oxygen. Because oxygen is not used, the process is called **anaerobic respiration**. Yeast is another organism that can carry out anaerobic respiration.

During anaerobic respiration, less energy is released than during aerobic respiration. This is because the glucose is only partly broken down. As well as carbon dioxide, alcohol may be formed as a waste product. This process is called **fermentation** and is used to make alcoholic drinks. The equation shows the reaction.

glucose → energy + carbon dioxide + alcohol

Bubbles of carbon dioxide show that bacteria are respiring in the mud, although there is very little oxygen there

Exercising hard

Larger organisms also respire anaerobically. If you are running flat out, you reach a point where you cannot take in oxygen any faster. You are making energy by aerobic respiration as fast as you can, but your body still needs more energy. At this point some of the glucose in your cells is broken down anaerobically to release a bit of extra energy. In animals the waste product is not alcohol but **lactic acid**. This is less poisonous than alcohol and so less damaging to cells. If too much lactic acid builds up in a muscle, it causes the muscle to go into spasm, which we call cramp. The spasm stops the muscle working, giving it time to recover.

Lactic acid is a large molecule which can provide a great deal of energy. When you stop exercising, the body turns most of the lactic acid back into glucose so that it can be respired aerobically. This process requires oxygen. The oxygen needed to convert lactic acid back into glucose is known as the **oxygen debt**. You will see athletes at the end of a race breathing fast and hard even though they have stopped running. This allows them to get the extra oxygen they need to remove the lactic acid.

Fast, deep breathing gets extra oxygen into the body to remove lactic acid

1. Where might you find organisms that respire anaerobically?

2. Animals produce lactic acid rather than alcohol in anaerobic respiration. What is the advantage in this?

3. Explain what is meant by the oxygen debt.

4. Germinating seeds often respire anaerobically to start with. Why might they need to do this?

Biotechnology

Biotechnology is using living things to make useful products for us. People have used biotechnology for thousands of years. In particular, people have used microbes which respire anaerobically (fermentation). People of nearly every culture throughout the world make alcoholic drinks. The discovery that yeast produces alcohol was probably made by accident. Many fruits have yeasts living on their surface. If people stored these fruits, the yeast could have fermented the sugar in the fruit, making a simple alcoholic drink. People may have tried this and enjoyed it!

The white covering on these grapes is yeast, which lives naturally on fruit

The modern fermentation of wine is carefully controlled

Making wine

Today wine- and beer-makers want their alcoholic drinks to be of reliable quality. They have to control the fermentation process. First they need a food source for the yeast. This food needs to be similar year after year if the drink is to be the same. People have spent many years developing grapes, hops, and other foods so that they have a reliable source. This food supply is then mixed with yeast and water and allowed to ferment. Yeasts have also been bred carefully to work in different conditions and on different foods. The yeast lives in the food supply until the alcohol level gets high enough to kill it. The drink formed contains alcohol made by the yeast, and flavour from the food source.

Making bread

Fermentation is also used in making bread. There are many different types of bread made throughout the world. Some are made with yeast. The yeast is mixed into the dough and starts to feed on the sugars in the flour. The yeast ferments the sugars and produces alcohol, along with carbon dioxide. As the dough is warmed, the carbon dioxide expands inside the dough. This causes bubbles which make the dough rise. When the bread is cooked, the yeast is killed and the alcohol is driven off. The bread has a light texture.

The chapatis (left) are made without yeast – unleavened. The loaf is made with yeast (right)

1. How does yeast feed naturally?
2. How might this have led to the invention of alcoholic drinks?
3. What conditions would it be important to control when making wine?
4. In the bottom photograph, explain why the bread on the right has a lighter texture than the bread on the left.
5. Find out how vinegar is made.

When seeds first germinate, they may be in a place where there is not much oxygen. They may be stuck in wet soil with little air. They get their energy for germination by respiring without oxygen. They transfer the energy in the bonds of glucose into ATP, so that they can use the energy. All processes that transfer energy are inefficient. Some of the energy is wasted as heat.

You can see how fast seeds are respiring by measuring the heat they produce. To do this you need to trap the heat by germinating some seeds in a vacuum flask. You can measure the temperature rise.

Instructions

1 Take some germinating seeds and rinse them in disinfectant and then distilled water. This will kill any microbes on the seeds. Their respiration would interfere with the results from the seeds.

2 Place the seeds in a vacuum flask.

3 Cover the seeds with cooled, boiled water and then a layer of oil.

(Boiling the water gets rid of any dissolved air, so removing the oxygen. The water must then be cooled to room temperature so you can measure any temperature rise caused by the seeds. The oil stops any oxygen dissolving in the water during the experiment. This guarantees that the seeds will be respiring without oxygen.)

4 Place a bung with a thermometer through it into the flask.

5 Set up a second flask in exactly the same way but without any seeds.

6 Read the temperature in both flasks. Take readings twice a day for a few days. Copy the table below and record your results.

(It may be possible for you to record continuous temperature readings using a data-logger and computer.)

7 What do your results show? What conclusions can you make?

8 a Is this experiment a fair test?

  b Should the second flask have had seeds in it?

  c If so, what should have been done to them?

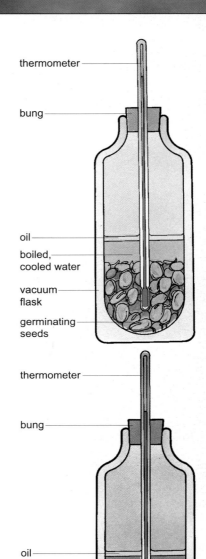

Time	Temperature/ °C	
	Flask with seeds	Flask without seeds

Plants and the atmosphere

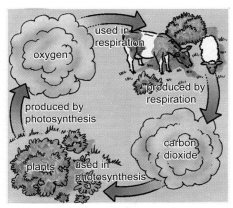

How respiration and photosynthesis affect the gases in the atmosphere

Detecting Carbon Dioxide

Carbon dioxide is slightly acidic when dissolved in water. The indicator turns yellow if there is more carbon dioxide (a more acidic solution). It turns mauve if there is less carbon dioxide (a less acidic solution).

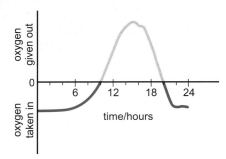

The graph shows the oxygen taken in and given out by a plant during one day

Producing oxygen

Plants were the first organisms to pollute the atmosphere. Before they evolved, the atmosphere would have contained mostly carbon dioxide, water vapour, and methane. Then photosynthesizing organisms started producing oxygen as a waste gas. This gradually built up in the atmosphere.

Investigating respiration and photosynthesis in plants

Respiration and photosynthesis are linked, as they both involve the same chemicals. Plants carry out both photosynthesis and respiration. A simple experiment shows this. A plant can be set up with its leaves placed in glass containers, without removing them from the plant. The containers have some indicator in them which shows whether carbon dioxide has been produced. Some containers are covered up, so the leaf is in darkness. Some containers only let through dim light. Some are uncovered, so the leaf is in bright light.

Amount of light	Indicator colour at start	Indicator colour at end	What does this tell you?
dark	red	yellow	more acidic – carbon dioxide produced
dim	red	red	no change
bright	red	mauve	less acidic – more oxygen and less carbon dioxide

What happens when plant leaves are kept at different light levels

In the dark, the leaves only respire. They get all their energy from the respiration of glucose. The process uses oxygen and produces carbon dioxide. In bright light the leaves photosynthesize. They use carbon dioxide and produce oxygen. Photosynthesis provides the leaf with energy so it does not respire very much. It gives out more oxygen than it uses.

In dim light, respiration and photosynthesis are balanced. The leaf is using as much carbon dioxide for photosynthesis as it makes by respiration. It is also using as much oxygen for respiration as it produces by photosynthesis. This means the air around it does not show any overall change.

1 Explain how respiration and photosynthesis interact in plants during daylight.

2 Why could plants be called the first polluters of the atmosphere?

3 Look at the graph on the left.

   a When are the processes of photosynthesis and respiration balanced?

   b Explain why they are not balanced at other times of day.

Transport in the body

All change

All living things are in a state of constant change. Every day your body takes in new chemicals and gets rid of wastes. Like a factory, you receive deliveries. Raw materials are taken into your body at certain points. They then have to be moved to where you need them. You also have despatch areas. In a factory these would be to send out products to customers. In your body they send out useful products and waste substances.

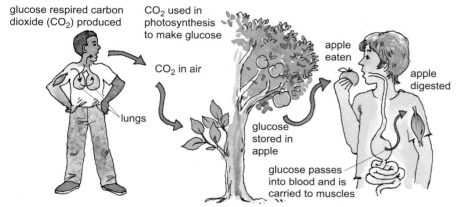

glucose respired carbon dioxide (CO_2) produced

CO_2 used in photosynthesis to make glucose

CO_2 in air

lungs

apple eaten

apple digested

glucose stored in apple

glucose passes into blood and is carried to muscles

The atoms in you are constantly changing. Chemically speaking, you will be almost completely different in ten years' time.

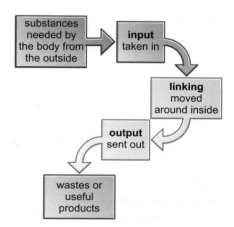

substances needed by the body from the outside

input taken in

linking moved around inside

output sent out

wastes or useful products

All organisms have transport systems

Transport systems

You have a variety of transport systems in your body to make sure things get to the right places. There are three sorts of system – **input systems**, **linking systems**, and **output systems**.

- Input systems include the gut and the lungs. The gut takes in food and the lungs take in oxygen from the environment.

- Linking systems include the blood and lymph systems. They carry substances around inside the body.

- Output systems include the gut, the lungs, the kidneys and bladder, and the reproductive system. They send substances out into the environment.

Integrated transport

It is important that all your body systems work together efficiently. It is a bit like an integrated transport system for road, rail, sea, and air. You need to be able to get from one part of the transport system to the other.

Your body's transport systems need to link together, like the roads, railways, and ferries at Dover

1 What are the three sorts of transport system?

2 Give one example of each sort of system in the body and say what it does.

3 Explain how a carbon atom in a glucose molecule inside you could become part of someone else.

Tube transport

The city of London has miles of underground tubes for transport. Your body also has a system of tubes for the same reason. The main transport system of the body is the **blood system**.

About blood ...

Blood is a mixture of **plasma** and **cells**. Plasma is a watery liquid containing dissolved chemicals. Food and wastes are carried in the plasma. There are two sorts of blood cell – **red blood cells** and **white blood cells**. Red blood cells carry oxygen and carbon dioxide around the body. White blood cells are the body's defence. They help fight diseases and infections caused by bacteria. Blood also contains some cell fragments called **platelets**. These help the blood to clot when you cut yourself. The clot seals over the cut and stops infections getting into your body.

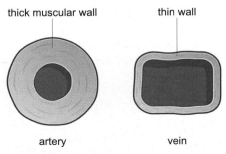
Blood seen under a scanning electron microscope magnified x2500 times.

... and the tubes that carry it

The tubes in your body that carry the blood are the **blood vessels**.

- **Arteries** carry blood away from the heart to all the other parts of the body. The blood is at high pressure. Arteries have strong muscular walls. They split into smaller arteries which link with capillaries.
- **Capillaries** are tiny tubes with walls only one cell thick. They form a network in all the body's organs. Their job is to allow materials to pass between the blood and the body's cells. The blood then flows through branches of larger tubes to the veins.
- **Veins** carry blood back to the heart. They have thinner walls than arteries because the blood is no longer under such high pressure. Veins below the heart have special valves in them to stop blood flowing backwards and keep it moving towards the heart.

artery

vein

thick muscular wall   thin wall

artery   vein

An artery and a vein

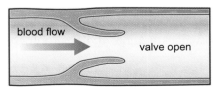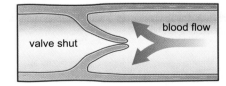
Valves in veins stop blood collecting in your feet!

1 What is blood?
2 What jobs does blood have to do?
3 Using the text and pictures, make a table of the differences between an artery and a vein.
4 Explain how vein valves work.

Did You Know?

There are hundreds of miles of blood vessels in your body!

The heart of the matter

A double pump

To transport substances, your blood has to be moved around your body. Blood is pumped around by the heart, a muscular pump. The heart actually contains two pumps, one on the left and one on the right. The right side pumps blood to the lungs, and the left side pumps blood to all other parts of the body. This system is called a **double circulation**. Both pumps must be co-ordinated for the blood to flow smoothly.

One-way system

Blood must only go through the circuit in one direction. The heart has valves between the different sections. Blood goes into the top chamber (atrium) through valves. It is pushed into the bottom chamber (ventricle) through another set of valves. Then it is pumped into the arteries leading away from the ventricles. There are more valves in these arteries. All these valves stop back-flow. The 'lub-dub' sound you hear when you listen to your heart is the valves slamming shut!

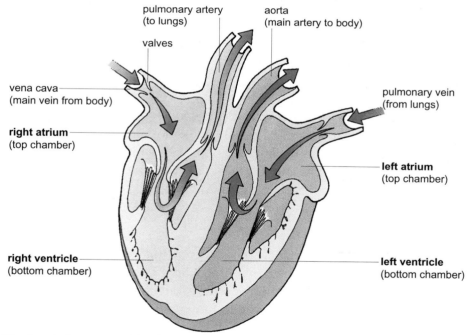

The heart of a mammal (such as you) is a double pump

> ### Did You Know?
>
> For many years, people in Europe thought the blood ebbed and flowed like the tide. However, the Chinese knew that blood circulated nearly 2000 years ago. The ideas came to Europe through an Arab scientist from Damascus called al-Nafis (died 1288).

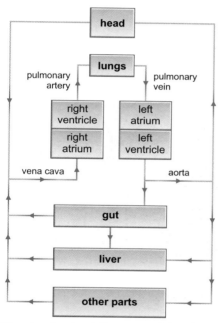

The double circulation – supplying the lungs and the rest of the body

> ### Did You Know?
>
> It takes about 30 seconds for blood to go once round the body.

1. Look at the diagram of the double circulation. Describe the route blood takes around the body, starting at the vena cava.

2. Why do you think the left ventricle has a thicker muscular wall than the right ventricle?

3. Why do you think we have two pumps and a double circulation?

4. Find out what is being measured when you have your blood pressure taken. How can blood pressure help tell a doctor whether you are healthy?

Changing places

Exchanging between blood and body cells

At a major railway station, people change from one train to another. The body's transport system also needs a changeover like this. When blood reaches an organ, it spreads out in the capillaries. These very small, thin vessels form a network through the organ. The blood moves under low pressure in the capillaries, so materials can be exchanged with the cells. Every cell in your body is very close to a capillary.

The blood has food and oxygen dissolved in it. The cells are busy working hard. They need food and oxygen. They make wastes, such as carbon dioxide, which need removing. The food and oxygen leave the blood and enter the cells. The wastes move the other way. Most of this exchange happens by diffusion.

The diagram on the left shows what happens in a capillary network.

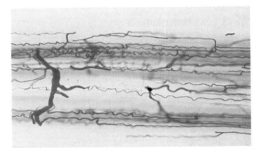

A capillary network in skeletal muscle, magnified x 100 times. Every organ contains a capillary network like this

blood brings food and oxygen

arteriole (small artery)

food

oxygen

body cell

capillary

carbon dioxide

venule (small vein)

▲ wastes

wastes

● oxygen

blood carries away carbon dioxide and wastes

✸ carbon dioxide

■ food

A capillary network is like a railway interchange, with substances moving in different directions

Transporting oxygen and carbon dioxide

Red blood cells contain a chemical called **haemoglobin**. This joins with oxygen in the lungs to form **oxyhaemoglobin**. In the organs, oxygen leaves the haemoglobin and passes into the cells. The haemoglobin picks up carbon dioxide and takes it back to the lungs.

Drainage

The capillary walls are so thin that some of the plasma leaks out between the cells. This liquid needs to be removed to stop it building up in the body tissues. Drainage tubes called **lymph vessels** collect the spare fluid and carry it away. Like the veins, the lymph vessels have valves to help stop back-flow. The collected fluid is called **lymph**. It is emptied from the lymph vessels into a vein in the neck. Lymph is different from blood in that it has no red blood cells and fewer proteins. These are too big to leak out through the walls of the capillaries.

Did You Know?

Along the lymph vessels are lymph glands where white blood cells fight infections. When you are ill, the lymph glands in your neck sometimes become swollen. The white blood cells are working hard to get rid of the infection.

1 What are the main functions of a capillary network?

2 Explain how oxygen and carbon dioxide are exchanged between the blood and the body cells.

3 Why do we need a drainage system for the fluid in the body tissues?

4 In what ways are blood and lymph different?

Finding out: The transport system

These simple practicals will help you to understand the structure and function of the blood system. You need to look carefully at what you see and try to decide why things are the way they are. Think about how the structures you see do the jobs they do.

Looking at the heart

1 Take a washed sheep's heart and lay it down facing you. Remove any excess fat. Can you see the arteries that feed the heart itself?

2 Cut carefully through the wall down both the left and right sides. This should allow you to open the chambers from the side.

3 a Which side has the thickest walls?

b What are the two valves between the upper and lower chambers like?

c Are they the same on both sides?

d Are the walls in the upper chamber smooth?

4 If they are present, cut open the big arteries leaving the heart. Look for the valves that stop blood flowing back.

5 How are these different from the valves between the chambers?

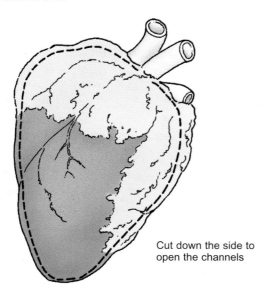

Cut down the side to open the channels

Looking at capillaries

It is possible to see capillaries in your own body. If you look at the base of your fingernail, you will see a white 'moon' section. Below this is a thin layer of pale transparent skin that edges the fingernail. This skin is the cuticle.

1 Wash your hands. Wipe a little oil over the cuticle of one finger. Wipe it onto your left hand if you are right handed (and vice versa).

2 Set up a microscope and shine a bench lamp onto the stage from above.

3 Put your oiled finger on the stage, as shown in the diagram above. Focus on the cuticle. You should be able to see the capillaries in this part of your finger.

a What patterns do they form?

b Make a careful drawing of what you see.

Looking at other blood vessels

1 Collect a prepared slide of a cross-section of an artery and a vein.

2 Look at it first under low power and then under high power. Make careful drawings of both vessels.

3 a What layers can you see in the walls?

b How are these different in the two sorts of vessel?

c How thick are the walls compared with the size of the vessel?

d Which vessel has the bigger centre hole compared with the size of the vessel?

20.01

REACTIVITY SERIES

Metals around you

The picture shows a street scene. Many of things in the picture are made of metals. The world would look very different if we did not have metals.

Replacing metals with new materials

Over the last 200 years, the world's population has grown rapidly. Everybody buys more and more goods such as cars, washing machines, and televisions. Many of these are made of metals or contain metal parts. As the demand for metals has increased, so the prices of metals have gone up. Plastics have replaced metals for many uses. Most of the plastics we use have been discovered in the past 60 years or so. They are made in large quantities from petroleum (crude oil). In a modern car, for example, there may be as many as 3000 different parts. Forty years ago most of these parts would have been made of metals. Now about one-third of them are plastic. Plastic parts are usually cheaper, easier to mould, and lighter in weight.

Until quite recently, all plastics were poor conductors of electricity. They could not replace metals that were being used to conduct electricity. An accidental discovery by scientists in Japan produced poly(ethyne), the first conducting plastic. Plastics now have even more uses.

For many large structures, concrete has replaced metals. Concrete is cheap and readily available. For example, concrete lamp-posts have replaced cast iron ones. Concrete is not a strong material on its own so it is usually reinforced with metal.

> **Did You Know?**
>
> The word 'metal' comes from an ancient Greek word meaning mine.

---

1 Make a list of ten things in the street scene made of metals.

2 What is special about the plastic called poly(ethyne)?

3 a Which label in the list opposite could be replaced by the word **malleable**?

   b Which could be replaced by the word **ductile**?

4 Below are some labels for properties of a material.

   Which labels refer to a metal and which do not? Make two lists.

- shiny surface when freshly cut
- can be drawn into fine wires
- good conductor of heat
- makes a ringing sound when struck
- low density

- may react with dilute acid to give off hydrogen
- can be beaten into thin sheets
- brittle
- poor conductor of electricity forms acidic oxides

Metals with water

Potassium and sodium are two metals. They are kept under paraffin oil to prevent air and water reacting with them.

This photograph shows a piece of potassium being cut with a knife. The cut surface is shiny at first, but it soon goes dull.

The second photograph shows a small piece of potassium reacting with water. The potassium floats on the water and reacts rapidly. The reaction produces hydrogen gas which burns with a pinkish purple flame. The other product is an alkali, potassium hydroxide, which dissolves in the water.

Sodium reacts in a similar way but more slowly. The hydrogen produced does not usually catch alight.

> ### Did You Know?
>
> The metals potassium and sodium have few uses because they are very reactive. Liquid sodium is used to cool nuclear reactors.

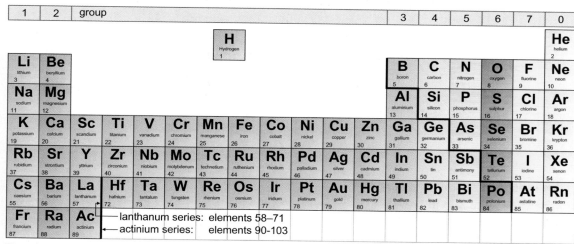

1	2	group													3	4	5	6	7	0

The Periodic Table of the elements

1. What causes the surface of sodium or potassium to go dull when it is cut?

2. The hydrogen formed when potassium reacts with cold water burns with a pinkish purple flame. What is formed when hydrogen burns?

3. Copy and complete the word equation for the reaction of potassium and cold water.

   potassium + water → _____ _____ + _____

4. How could you detect the alkali in the water at the end of the reaction of potassium with water?

5. What is the alkali formed when sodium reacts with cold water?

6. When sodium is produced in large amounts industrially, the lumps are wrapped in polythene instead of being stored under oil. Why is sodium packed in polythene?

7. Look at the Periodic Table above. Sodium and potassium are in the same family of elements (the same vertical column). Which other metals would you expect to react with cold water?

Finding out: Lithium, calcium with water

In this experiment you are going to react small pieces of lithium and calcium with cold water. Your teacher will cut the lithium for you.

Instructions

1 Half fill the beaker with cold water. Fill the test tube with cold water and put a cork into the tube.

2 Turn the test tube upside down and remove the cork from the tube under water.

3 Drop the piece of lithium in the water and cover the lithium with the test tube as shown in the diagram. Write down what you see. You will be able to collect the gas produced when lithium and water react.

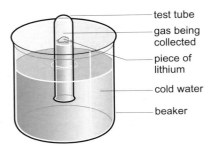

- test tube
- gas being collected
- piece of lithium
- cold water
- beaker

4 When the test tube is full of gas, put the cork back in it under water. Test the gas in the tube by removing the cork and putting a lighted splint into the tube.

5 Add a couple of drops of universal indicator to the water in the beaker.

6 Repeat the process with a piece of calcium.

7 Copy and complete the table below.

Metal	Observations
lithium	
calcium	

8 Does the lithium sink or float? What does this tell you?

9 Does the calcium sink or float? What does this tell you?

10 What happens when a lighted splint is put into a test tube of the gas?

11 Which gas have you collected?

12 What colour does the universal indicator turn? What does this show you?

13 Copy and complete the word equations for the reactions.

lithium + water → _____ + _____

calcium + water → _____ + _____

WARNING

Wear safety goggles
Do not handle lithium or calcium with your hands.

Reactivity series

Who will win?

Predicting the result of a football match is very difficult to do. The best guide is usually to compare previous results. In a match between the team at the top of the league and the team at the bottom, it would be likely that the team at the top would win.

A league table of metals

We can arrange metals in a league according to the results of reactions. For example, we might react different metals with water, or with acid, and note how quickly each metal reacts. We call this league a **reactivity series**. The metal at the top of the reactivity series is most reactive. The metal at the bottom of the reactivity series is least reactive.

The reactivity series is useful for predicting which reactions might take place.

A fair test for reactivity

To compare the reactivity of different metals, it is important to use a **fair test**. This is to make sure the only difference between the reactions is the different metals. The following experiment shows how you can get different results even with the same metal, if you do not use a fair test.

The diagram shows four test tubes. They each contain an equal volume of dilute hydrochloric acid. The metal in each is iron, but it is in different forms.

- In A it is a single lump.
- In B it is a fine powder.
- In C it is in small pieces.
- In D it is in large pieces.

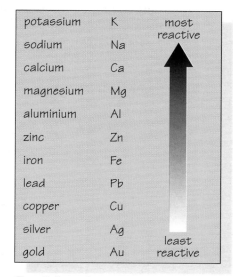

potassium	K	most reactive
sodium	Na	
calcium	Ca	
magnesium	Mg	
aluminium	Al	
zinc	Zn	
iron	Fe	
lead	Pb	
copper	Cu	
silver	Ag	
gold	Au	least reactive

Reactivity series

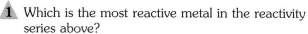
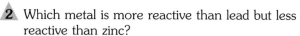

A   B   C   D

You can get different results with the same metal if you do not have a fair test

 1 Which is the most reactive metal in the reactivity series above?

2 Which metal is more reactive than lead but less reactive than zinc?

3 How many metals in the list are more reactive than zinc?

4 Note your observations about the reactions in the four test tubes.

5 Explain the differences.

Finding out: Metals with acid

In this experiment you are going to compare the reactions of four metals with dilute hydrochloric acid. You will be able to arrange the four metals in order of reactivity. The four metals are copper, iron, magnesium, and zinc.

Instructions

1 Put a piece of magnesium into a test tube and add 5 cm depth of dilute hydrochloric acid. If there is no reaction, or the reaction is very slow, heat the test tube. Test any gas with a lighted splint. A squeaky pop is a positive test for hydrogen gas.

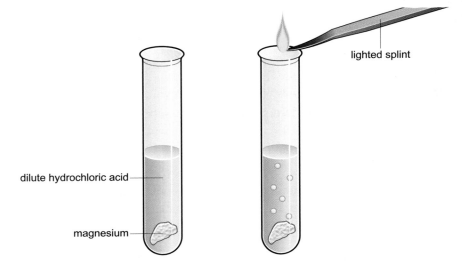

lighted splint

dilute hydrochloric acid

magnesium

2 Repeat the experiment with each of the metals in turn. Make sure you use the same amount of each metal.

3 Copy and complete the table below.

4 List the four metals in order of reactivity, with the most reactive metal first.

5 In this experiment you have carried out a **fair test**. You kept some things the same in each test. Write down three things you kept the same.

Metal	Without heating	On heating
magnesium		
iron		
copper		
zinc		

Displacement reactions

Who will win?

The old man on the right is carrying a large amount of money. If he is attacked by the robber he is almost certain to have the money stolen. The robber is more powerful.

We could summarize this in an equation.

old man with money + robber → old man + robber with money

The security man is well prepared. The would-be robber is going to be unsuccessful.

Metals competing

It is like this when two metals compete in a chemical reaction. If an iron nail is put into copper(II) sulphate solution, a reaction slowly takes place. The iron nail becomes coated with copper. (If the solution is in excess the colour changes from blue to colourless.) The iron takes the place of the copper in the copper(II) sulphate – it 'steals' the sulphate. This is called a **displacement reaction**. The iron **displaces** the copper.

The reaction can be summarized in this equation.

copper(II) sulphate + iron → copper + iron(II) sulphate

The reaction takes place because iron is more powerful (or reactive) than copper. Iron is higher in the reactivity series.

If an iron nail is put into zinc sulphate solution, no reaction takes place. This is because iron is less reactive than zinc. It is lower in the reactivity series.

Did You Know?

A displacement reaction between aluminium powder and iron oxide is used to weld lengths of railway track.

---

 1 A piece of iron is placed in each of six test tubes. Each test tube contains a different solution. They are

- magnesium sulphate
- sodium chloride
- silver nitrate
- zinc sulphate
- copper(II) sulphate
- lead(II) nitrate.

In which test tubes will a reaction take place?

2 Write word summaries (**word equations**) for the reactions taking place when magnesium is added to

a copper(II) sulphate

b lead(II) nitrate.

Finding out: Metals in order

In this experiment you are going to arrange five metals in order of reactivity. You will use the reaction of the metals with acid, and also displacement reactions. The five metals are iron, cobalt, copper, manganese, and nickel.

Instructions

1 Put one spatula measure of iron into a test tube and add 5 cm depth of dilute hydrochloric acid. If there is no reaction, or the reaction is very slow, heat the test tube. Note the colour of the final solution and test any gas with a lighted splint. A squeaky pop is a positive test for hydrogen gas.

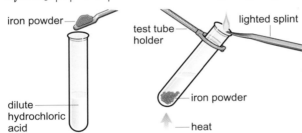

2 Put 3 cm depth of copper(II) sulphate solution, nickel(II) sulphate solution, iron(II) sulphate solution, and manganese(II) sulphate solution into separate test tubes. Add one spatula measure of cobalt powder to each test tube. Note the colours of the solutions at the start and also again a day later.

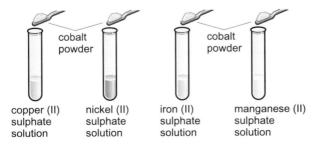

3 Copy and complete the following tables.

Metal	Without heating	On heating
iron		
cobalt		
copper		
manganese		
nickel		

Reaction of metals with hydrochloric acid

Metal salt solution	Colour of solution at start	Colour of solution at least one day later
copper(II) sulphate		
nickel(II) sulphate		
iron(II) sulphate		
manganese(II) sulphate		

Displacement reaction

4 List the five metals in order of reactivity, with the most reactive metal first.

5 Look at the Periodic Table on page 23. Can you see any connection between the reactivity of these five metals and their positions in the Periodic Table?

Stable compounds

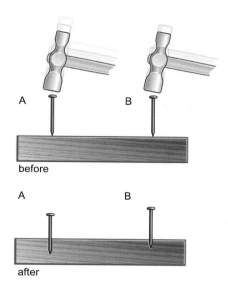

Hit it with a hammer

Have you ever tried to pull a nail out of a piece of wood? How difficult this is depends on how far the nail is pushed into the wood. Nail A in the diagram is hit once hard. Nail B is hit once with the same hammer, but more gently. Nail A goes much further into the wood and so is more difficult to remove.

Stable or unstable?

It is a bit like this with compounds of metals. Some are formed in a reaction where a lot of energy is released. Like moving nail A, splitting up these compounds is difficult. Other compounds are formed in a reaction where little or no energy is released. Like moving nail B, splitting up these compounds is easy. A compound that is difficult to split up is called a **stable** compound, and one that is easy to split up is called an **unstable** compound.

Reactive metals make stable compounds

Metals high in the reactivity series form stable compounds which are difficult to split up. Metals low in the reactivity series form unstable compounds which either do not exist or are split up easily.

The table compares the stability of metal nitrates and metal carbonates on heating. It shows the **thermal decomposition** reactions of these compounds (the reactions that split up the compounds when they are heated).

Compound of	Carbonate	Nitrate
potassium	not decomposed	oxygen is lost at high temperatures; the metal nitrite remains
sodium	not decomposed	
calcium		
magnesium	decomposed into the metal oxide and carbon dioxide	decomposed into the metal oxide, brown nitrogen dioxide gas, and oxygen gas
zinc		
iron	carbonates become easier to decompose as you move down the list	
lead		
copper		
silver	carbonate is not stable at room temperature	decomposed into the metal, nitrogen dioxide, and oxygen

Did You Know?

Potassium carbonate and sodium carbonate are not decomposed even when they are heated to one million degrees centigrade.

 1 Look at the list below:

a Choose from the list the metal that will release the most energy when it reacts with oxygen.

> **calcium   copper   lead   magnesium   potassium   zinc**

b Why did you make this choice?

c Choose from the same list the metal that will release the least energy when it reacts with oxygen.

d Why did you make this choice?

2 Look at the table above. Write word equations for the thermal decomposition of

a calcium carbonate   **b** sodium nitrate

c zinc nitrate   **d** silver nitrate.

Extracting aluminium and iron

Metals occur naturally in the Earth, in **ores**. We have to extract the metal from its ore before we can use it. Metals high in the reactivity series form stable compounds. These compounds need a lot of energy to split them up. This is done by a process called **electrolysis**. Metals lower in the reactivity series form less compounds and can be extracted more easily.

Extraction of aluminium

Aluminium is extracted from the Earth in an ore called **bauxite**. Bauxite is purified to form alumina (aluminium oxide). The aluminium oxide is dissolved in molten cryolite (sodium aluminium fluoride) for electrolysis. The steel lining of the cell is the negative electrode. The positive electrodes are made of carbon. The cell is shown in the diagram on the left. Electrolysis splits the aluminium oxide into aluminium and oxygen. Aluminium is produced at the negative electrode and oxygen at the positive electrode. The aluminium collects at the bottom of the cell and can be run off through a tap.

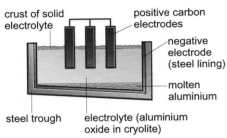

crust of solid electrolyte

positive carbon electrodes

negative electrode (steel lining)

molten aluminium

steel trough

electrolyte (aluminium oxide in cryolite)

Aluminium is extracted from its ore by electrolysis in a cell like this

Extraction of iron

Iron is extracted from an ore containing iron(III) oxide. This process takes place in a **blast furnace**. The diagram on the left shows a blast furnace.

The blast furnace is loaded with iron ore, coke (carbon), and limestone (calcium carbonate). Blasts of hot air are blown into the bottom of the furnace. Some of the carbon is burnt and carbon monoxide is formed. This is the **reducing agent** in the furnace. It removes oxygen from the iron(III) oxide.

The limestone decomposes in the furnace to produce calcium oxide. This calcium oxide reacts with silicon(IV) oxide (sand), an impurity in the ore. It produces calcium silicate (called slag). This floats on the iron and is removed.

Molten iron and molten slag are tapped off from the furnace from time to time. These word equations summarize the reactions in the blast furnace.

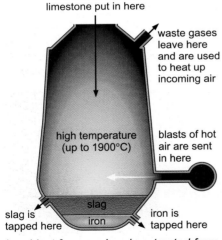

iron ore, coke, and limestone put in here

waste gases leave here and are used to heat up incoming air

high temperature (up to 1900°C)

blasts of hot air are sent in here

slag is tapped here

slag

iron

iron is tapped here

In a blast furnace, iron is extracted from iron(III) oxide by heating the ore with carbon and calcium carbonate

(1) carbon + oxygen → carbon dioxide

(2) carbon dioxide + carbon → carbon monoxide

(3) iron(III) oxide + carbon monoxide → iron + carbon dioxide

(4) calcium carbonate → calcium oxide + carbon dioxide

(5) calcium oxide + silicon(IV) oxide → calcium silicate

1 Aluminium is extracted from its ore by electrolysis. Write down the names of three other metals which you would expect to be extracted by electrolysis.

2 Which equation above summarizes the important reaction in the blast furnace?

3 The carbon anodes have to be replaced frequently during the extraction of aluminium. Why do you think this is?

4 Give two reasons for adding limestone to the furnace.

5 Why is electrolysis needed to extract aluminium, while iron can be extracted without it?

Preventing corrosion

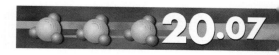

Metals can react with oxygen and water in the atmosphere. This type of reaction is called **corrosion**. Corrosion is an oxidation process in which electrons are lost. Iron corrodes and forms rust, a type of iron oxide. Steel is iron with other substances added to it. Some steel rusts too.

Rusting of iron and steel is a big problem because these metals are used to build many structures.

There are several ways of slowing down the rusting of iron or steel.

Pure iron and alloys

Iron that is very pure does not rust. The photograph on the right shows a column in Delhi in India. Although this iron column is many centuries old, it shows no signs of rusting because the iron is very pure. It is very expensive to make iron this pure.

Iron can be mixed with other metals such as chromium to form an alloy called stainless steel. This rusts less than the iron or steel commonly used for building. Unfortunately pure iron and stainless steel are both very expensive.

Coating

Rusting is slowed down by coating with oil, grease, paint, or plastic. The coating provides a barrier to prevent air and water coming into contact with the metal. If this barrier is broken down, rusting starts. Sometimes steel is coated with zinc. This is called galvanized steel. It is useful for wire fences.

Sacrificial protection

This illustration right shows the hull of a steel ship. It is always in sea water. It cannot be painted under water. Lumps of a reactive metal such as magnesium are attached to the hull. The magnesium corrodes instead of the steel. This is called **sacrificial protection**. The magnesium lumps can easily be replaced.

A way of protecting pier legs is to use steel electrodes connected to an electrical supply. The legs are kept negative. This prevents the steel rusting.

1 Suggest conditions which might make iron and steel rust quickly.

2 Most car bodies are attached to the negative terminal of the battery. What is the advantage of doing this?

The Delhi column in India does not rust because the iron it is made of is pure

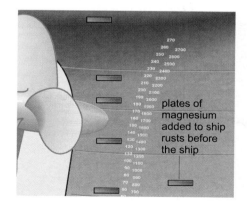
plates of magnesium added to ship rusts before the ship

Finding out: Pairs of metals

In this experiment you will compare the corrosion of different pairs of metals in contact. A pair of metals in contact is called a **couple**. You will use the following pairs of metals.

- iron and zinc
- iron and tin
- copper and zinc
- iron and magnesium
- iron and copper
- aluminium and iron

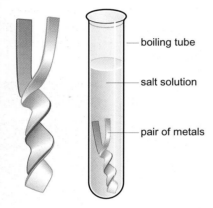

boiling tube

salt solution

pair of metals

Instructions

1 Clean both metals with emery paper and wash them with distilled water. Tightly twist the two metals together as shown. Drop the metals together into a boiling tube. Add enough salt solution to just cover them. Do this for each metal pair.

2 Look at the metals in the boiling tubes carefully after about an hour. Look again after a day or so. Observe the changes taking place on each metal.

3 Copy and complete the table below.

Your teacher will have some test tubes containing the individual metals in salt solution. You may use these for comparison.

Pair of metals	Observations
iron and zinc	
iron and tin	
copper and zinc	
iron and magnesium	
iron and copper	
aluminium and iron	

4 If two metals are coupled together and put in salt solution, how can you predict which metal will corrode?

Cycling

Getting the best out of your bicycle

Answer these questions *honestly*. How often do you do these things?

- have your bike serviced?
- check the wear of the brake shoes?
- check that the wheels are turning freely?
- lubricate the gears and drive mechanism?
- check the pressure of the air in the tyres?
- check the tread on the tyres?

The driving force

How well a bicycle speeds up, brakes, and how fast it goes all depend on forces. There are two types of force that act on a bicycle. The force that pushes the bicycle forwards is called the **driving force**. If you are travelling along a level road without any wind to help you, you have to pedal. The force you exert on the pedal is transmitted through the chain and gears to the back wheel. Here, friction between the wheel and the road gives the driving force – the push of the road on the tyre.

The force that drives a bicycle starts with your foot on the pedal, but it acts at the back wheel where the road pushes you along

Resistive forces

While you are going forwards, **resistive forces** are pushing back on you all the time. **Air resistance** is the main one. You can minimize this by bending low over the handlebars. **Rolling resistance** comes from the tyres reshaping as they turn. Keeping them at the correct pressure reduces rolling resistance. There is also **friction** in the wheel bearings. These should be checked when you have the bicycle serviced.

Resistive forces include air resistance, rolling resistance, and friction forces

Braking

If you have to brake sharply then you need a lot of friction between the brake blocks and the wheel rim, as well as between the tyres and the road surface. Your safety depends on the condition of your brakes and tyres.

> ### Did You Know?
>
> Two-wheeled propulsion machines were first invented in the early 1600s. The first bicycle that could be steered was invented in 1816, and the modern bicycle dates from 1869.

1 a Explain how friction is needed to drive a bicycle along.

b Why is friction needed to stop a bicycle?

2 a Describe and explain what would happen if you tried to cycle on a low-friction surface such as ice.

b Describe and explain how wet weather affects the braking of a bicycle.

3 Imagine that you own a bicycle maintenance and repair shop. Design a display advertisement for your local newspaper offering free safety checks on bicycles.

Who won the race?

Abigail

Nikki

Hamel

starting line

Brian

A fair test?

Four young children were having a race. They marked out a starting line and a finishing line. Brian was younger than the others so they gave him a start. Abigail was tall with long legs, so she had a handicap. The diagram shows how they started the race.

Nikki crossed the finishing line first, followed by Abigail and then Brian. Hamel was last to finish.

The children could not agree who was the fastest runner. They ran the race again, but this time they got some friends to time how long each runner took to complete the race. The table below shows the times.

The children agreed that Nikki had won both races, but they still could not decide who was the fastest runner.

Improving the test

Abigail took longer than Nikki to complete the race, but she had further to travel. Brian finished before Hamel, but he ran a shorter distance. To find out who is the fastest runner, the children all need to run the same distance. The fastest runner is the person who finishes first and completes the race in the shortest time.

Runner	Time taken to complete race/s	Runner	Time taken to complete race/s
Abigail	13.0	Hamel	15.5
Brian	14.5	Nikki	12.5

1 a How was Brian given a start in the race?

b What was Abigail's handicap?

c Explain why the children thought it fair to give Brian a start and Abigail a handicap.

2 In the second race, you can compare the speeds of two of the runners.

a Whose speeds can you compare?

b Which of the two was faster? How can you can tell?

c Four people timed the runners in the second race. Write out a set of instructions to the timers so that their recorded times are as reliable as possible.

3 Four teams compete in a 400 m relay race. There are four runners in a team and each person runs 100 m. The table below shows the time taken for each runner to complete 100 m.

Team	Runner 1	Runner 2	Runner 3	Runner 4
red	13.6	14.1	15.4	12.6
green	14.7	15.2	13.1	12.8
blue	12.9	15.6	13.3	14.4
yellow	13.1	12.7	14.2	14.0

a Which team was ahead after 100 m?

b Which team was ahead after 200 m?

c Which team won the race?

d Which team had the fastest runner?

e Which team had the slowest runner?

Speed traps

Kill your speed

Signs by the road show the speed limit for cars and other traffic. However, motorists often ignore them and drive too fast. This is dangerous. There are a number of other ways of slowing down the traffic.

One way is to build 'sleeping policemen'. These are humps in the road surface. Driving too fast over the humps may damage the car, so drivers slow down.

'Sleeping policemen' slow down the traffic

Trapping speeding motorists

The police use infra-red beams to detect speeding motorists. Two beams can time a car as it travels a measured distance. The shorter the time taken, the faster the car is travelling. A camera takes a photograph of the car number plate, and motorists who exceed the speed limits are caught.

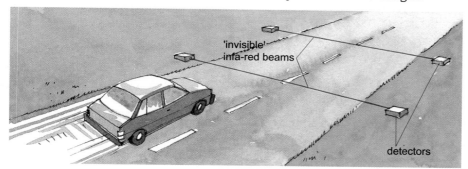

'invisible' infra-red beams

detectors

Did You Know?

The fastest car on Earth broke the sound barrier. It set a new world record for speed on the ground in 1997. It was powered by a jet engine and reached a speed greater than 750 m.p.h.

Working out the speed

Two measurements are needed to work out the speed. One is the time taken for the car to travel between the two infra-red beams. The other is the distance between the beams. The speed of a car is calculated on the right.

The unit 'm/s' is read as 'metres per second'. If the car keeps on travelling at this speed, it will cover a distance of 8 m each second. It is important to give the correct units when you give a speed.

Example

distance travelled by car = 4.0 m

time taken = 0.50 s

$$\text{speed of car} = \frac{\text{distance travelled}}{\text{time taken}}$$

$$= \frac{4.0 \text{ m}}{0.5 \text{ s}}$$

$$= 8.0 \text{ m/s}$$

---

1. Which two pieces of information are needed to work out the speed of a runner? Choose from the list below.

   A the height of the runner

   B the distance that the runner travels

   C the weight of the runner

   D the time taken to travel the distance

2. a A bicycle travels 20 m in 5 s. Work out the speed of the bicycle.

   b A bus travels 400 m in 80 s. Work out the speed of the bus.

   c A milk float travels 60 m in 120 s. Work out the speed of the milk float.

3. A car travels 200 miles in 5 hours.

   a Work out the average speed of the car.

   b Explain why this is an average speed.

To work out the speed of a moving object, you need to know both the distance and the time. One way to measure speed is to time the object as it travels a measured distance.

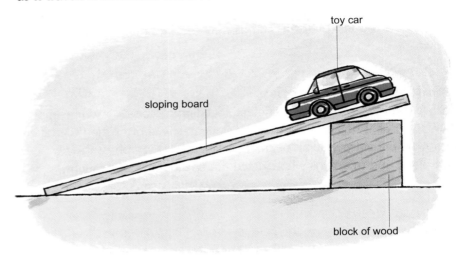

Instructions

1 Hold a toy car at the top of a sloping board.

2 Release the car and time how long it takes to reach the bottom of the slope.

3 Repeat this twice so that you have three separate timings. If they are not close together, carry on repeating until you have three readings that are close. Then use these to work out an average time for the car to travel down the slope.

4 Measure the distance that the car travelled. Work out its average speed using this equation.

$$\text{average speed} = \frac{\text{distance travelled}}{\text{time taken}}$$

5 How does the average speed of the car depend on the distance that the car travels down the slope? Write down your prediction, together with a reason.

6 Take a series of measurements to test your prediction. Record your results in a table like this example on the right.

7 Use your results to plot a graph of distance travelled against average speed.

8 Does your graph show a relationship between the distance travelled by the car and the average speed? Explain how you can tell from the graph.

9 Does the relationship agree with your prediction? Try to explain the relationship that you have found.

Distance travelled/cm	Time/s			Average time/s	Average speed /cm/s
	1	2	3		

Journey times

Wherever you are going, if you are to arrive on time you need to know how long the journey will take so that you can set off in time.

How fast can you travel?

The answer to this question depends on whether you are walking, cycling, or in a car. It also depends on the type of road, and it can even depend on the time of day and the day of the week.

Driving around town, a car averages a speed of about 25 m.p.h. (11 m/s) and a cyclist about 8 m.p.h. (3.5 m/s). The average speed in a city is usually slower, because there is more traffic and more traffic lights, and queues slow you down.

The average speed on a motorway is usually faster, about 60 m.p.h. (27 m/s) if there are no hold-ups. It is faster still to travel by air.

A traffic jam reduces the average speed

The journey time

The journey time depends on the average speed. It also depends on how far you have to go. The further the distance, the longer it takes. You can use the speed equation in a different form to work out journey times. The example on the right shows how.

Take care with the units. In the example the speed is in m.p.h. and the distance in miles, so the time is worked out in hours. When measuring speed in science, you are more likely to use the units metres (m) for distance, seconds (s) for time, and metres per second (m/s) for speed.

This aircraft takes people on holiday at a speed of about 550 m.p.h.

Example

The distance from Leeds to London is 200 miles. A driver travels at an average speed of 50 m.p.h. How long does the journey take?

Answer

$$\text{time} = \frac{\text{distance travelled}}{\text{average speed}}$$

$$= \frac{200 \text{ miles}}{50 \text{ m.p.h.}}$$

$$= 4 \text{ hours}$$

1. Explain why the average speed of a car is usually greater when travelling on a motorway than when travelling in a town.

2. Calculate the times for the following journeys.

   a 2400 m by bicycle at an average speed of 12 m/s

   b 575 km by car at an average speed of 50 km/h

   c 4500 miles by air at an average speed of 500 m.p.h.

3. I am going to Spain on my holidays. The flight leaves at 10.30 a.m. I need to arrive at least 2 hours before take-off. The distance from my home to the airport is 125 miles. I expect to do the journey to the airport at an average speed of 50 m.p.h. What is the latest time that I should leave home?

Did You Know?

Before the railways were built, a journey from London to York by stagecoach took two days. It now takes two hours.

Speed and safety

How fast is safe?

On most roads where there are a lot of houses, in built-up areas, cars should not travel faster than 30 m.p.h. At a speed of 30 m.p.h. a car travels more than 13 m in one second.

A car travelling at 30 m.p.h. travels this distance in 1 second

13 m

Drivers face a number of hazards when driving in built-up areas. The car in front may stop or swerve suddenly. Pedestrians pose particular dangers, especially when they are small children! The picture below shows a driver's view of a young child waiting to cross the road. Can you see the child? No, and nor can the driver!

child is here

Whatever speed a car is travelling at, it cannot stop instantly. There is no safe speed. People can be killed or injured by slow or fast-moving vehicles.

thinking distance = 9 m   braking distance = 14 m

Stopping distances

When a driver sees a hazard in the road, it takes some time to react. This is called the driver's **reaction time**. After the driver has put on the brakes, the car travels some distance before it stops. This distance depends on several things, including the speed of the car.

The diagram on the left shows the **stopping distance** for a car travelling at 30 m.p.h. The stopping distance is made up of

- the **thinking distance**, which is how far the car travels before the driver applies the brakes, and

- the **braking distance**, which is how far the car travels after the brakes are applied before it stops.

The longer the stopping distance, the less chance the driver has of avoiding an accident. Many injuries in road accidents are caused by drivers travelling too fast, so they have a long stopping distance.

---

1 a What is meant by a 'built-up area'?

b List five hazards for a driver to think about when driving in a built-up area.

2 a What factors might affect a driver's reaction time?

b Explain why the manufacturers of some medicines recommend that people using the medicine should not drive.

3 The diagram below shows the stopping distance for a car travelling at 60 m.p.h. Compare this with the stopping distance for a car travelling at 30 m.p.h. above.

a What is the relationship between speed and thinking distance?

b What is the relationship between speed and braking distance?

thinking distance = 18 m   braking distance = 42 m

total stopping distance = 60 m

Starting a race

If you are running in a race on sports day, do you have a favourite starting position?

A staggered start

In a 100 m race, you normally run along a straight track, so that the start and finish lines are the same for everyone. But in a 400 m race, the track curves. The person on the outside of the curve runs further than the person on the inside. To allow for this, the starting lines are usually staggered so that everyone runs the same distance to the finish line. However, this may not make it completely fair!

The starting pistol

The signal to start a race is usually a loud noise, for example from a starting pistol. With staggered start lines, one runner is quite a lot nearer to the pistol. It takes time for sound to travel, so this person hears the pistol first and sets off first. The runner who is furthest away from the starting pistol is the last to hear the signal.

How great is the advantage?

At the beginning of a 400 m race, the runner nearest to the starter is 10 m from the pistol. The runner furthest away is 50 m from the pistol. How long does it take for the sound to travel the extra 40 m? The example on the right shows how to work this out.

The runner nearest to the starter has an advantage of 0.125 s. This might make a difference if there is a close finish to the race.

> ### Did You Know?
>
> The Olympic games were officially founded at Olympia in Greece in 776 BC. They were held in honour of the god Zeus.

Example

First you need to know how fast sound travels. In air at ground level, it travels at 320 m/s.

Then you need to use the speed equation to calculate the journey time:

$$\text{time} = \frac{\text{distance travelled}}{\text{speed}}$$

$$= \frac{40 \text{ m}}{320 \text{ m/s}} = 0.125 \text{ s}$$

---

1 Explain why the start lines are staggered in a 400 m race.

2 In a 100 m race, the runners start along a straight line. The starter stands on the inside of the track alongside the runners.

  a Which runner is the first to hear the starting pistol?

  b Where should the starter stand to make it a fairer start? Explain how this would make it fairer.

The people timing the race stand opposite the finishing line. They start their watches when they hear the sound from the pistol.

  c How long does it take for the sound from the pistol to reach the timers?

  d Suggest a fairer way of timing the race.

3 When you look at a low-flying aircraft at night, the sound and its lights seem to come from different places.

  a Explain why the sound and light seem to come from different places.

  b Explain why this does not happen when you look at a moving car.

Speed and graphs

How can you compare speeds at different points in a journey? One way is to use the speed equation to work out the speeds. To get a picture of a whole journey, it is useful to study a graph of the motion.

A bicycle ride

On a bicycle ride, the distance that you have travelled is increasing all the time. Even if you turn around and go home, the total distance that you have travelled continues to increase.

The graph above shows how the total distance travelled by a cyclist changes during a short cycle ride. There are four sections to the graph, labelled **A**, **B**, **C**, and **D**. The speed is different in each section of the graph. You can work out the average speed of the cyclist in each section using the equation

$$\text{average speed} = \frac{\text{distance travelled}}{\text{time taken}}$$

In section **B**, the total distance travelled by the cyclist increases from 100 m to 420 m. So the distance travelled in this part of the bicycle ride is 420 − 100 = 320 m. The time taken to travel this distance is 60 − 20 = 40 s. So

$$\text{average speed for section } \mathbf{B} = \frac{320 \text{ m}}{40 \text{ s}} = 8 \text{ m/s}$$

Work out the average speed for sections **A**, **C**, and **D** of the graph. You should notice that the steeper the graph line, the greater the speed.

The gradient represents the speed

On a graph of total distance travelled against time taken, the slope or **gradient** of the graph represents the speed. So you can compare speeds in different parts of a journey by comparing the gradient of the line in different sections.

Did You Know?

The bicycle is one of the most efficient forms of transport. Energy from the pedals is transferred to the driving wheel with an efficiency of 98.5%.

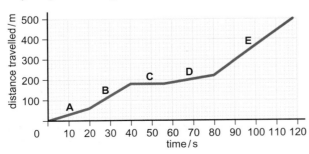

The graph below shows how the distance travelled by a cyclist changes with time.

1 a In which sections of the graph was the cyclist moving?

b How long did the cyclist spend at rest?

c Which section of the graph represents the fastest speed? Explain how you can tell.

2 a During the ride, the cyclist went up a steep hill. Which section of the graph represents this part of the ride? Explain how you can tell.

b Explain which part of the graph is most likely to show the cyclist travelling downhill.

3 a Calculate the average speed of the cyclist in each section of the graph.

b Calculate the average speed for the whole bicycle ride. Explain why this is an *average* speed.

Taking home the shopping

Have you ever noticed that a bag of shopping seems to get heavier the further you carry it? It does not really get heavier, but your muscles get tired and start to ache. A heavy bag of shopping can easily weigh up to 50 N, and that will not just make your arms ache, it could also hurt your hands.

Shopping bags

Shopping bags come in different shapes and sizes, but they all have one thing in common – handles! The diagram below shows three types of handle.

The carrier bags given away by supermarkets have polythene handles. Some bags have handles made out of string, and others have handles made from a wide strip of canvas or plastic.

Spreading the load

Carrying shopping in a bag with string handles can make you feel as if the string is cutting into your hands. Bags with wider handles are more comfortable, because the force (the weight of the bag) is spread over a larger area. Spreading a force over a large area makes it less likely to cut into things.

Bags with string handles are suitable for shopping that does not weigh very much. Even though the force is concentrated on a small area, the force is small. It does not cause the string to cut into your hands. For heavier shopping, you need wider handles to spread the force out so you can carry it comfortably.

1 Which type of shopping bag would you choose to carry home 5 kg of potatoes? Explain your choice.

2 List six items of shopping that you could carry together comfortably in a bag with string handles. Explain why you chose them.

3 Explain why a heavy bag with thin handles cuts into your hand, but one with wide handles does not.

Did You Know?

Supermarket carrier bags cause litter problems in this country and abroad. Many supermarkets now sell a 'bag for life' which they replace free if it wears out.

Force and area

Everything we do involves forces. You use forces to move yourself around, to eat, and to breathe.

Feeding with forces

When you eat, you use forces to cut food with a knife and pierce it with a fork. A knife blade has a very small area in contact with the food. The sharper the knife, the smaller this area is and the better the knife cuts. The prongs of a fork also have a very small area so a force can push the fork into the food easily.

Under pressure

A force that acts over a small area can cut or pierce because of its high **pressure**. The pressure a force causes depends on both the size of the force and the area that it acts over. Drawing pins and nails are designed so that the force acts on a small area. This causes a large pressure on the surface, so the pin or nail pierces the surface.

Reducing the pressure

People who ski do not want to sink into the snow. They spread their weight out over a large area. Spreading out a force over a larger area reduces the pressure that it causes, so it is less likely to pierce the surface that it acts on. Builders working on a fragile roof use a board to move around on. Their weight exerts a small pressure on the roof, so the roof does not give way under them.

Ice skating

Ice skaters skate on water! Their weight pushes down on the narrow blades of the skates, causing a high pressure. This melts the ice around the blades. This is why skaters can glide through solid ice. The tracks they leave are ice that has melted and re-frozen when the pressure is removed.

Did You Know?

It is possible for a person to lie on broken glass without puncturing the skin (but don't try it yourself!). Many pieces of blunt glass give a large area to spread the body weight over.

The force from the hammer is concentrated on the small tip of the nail, causing a large pressure

The skis spread out the force over a large area, causing a small pressure on the snow

The large pressure on an ice skate melts the ice underneath

1 a List three examples of forces being used to create a large pressure to cut or pierce something.

   b List three examples of forces acting over a large area to avoid cutting or piercing something.

2 a Explain why a drawing pin needs to have a sharp point.

   b Why do skis need to have a large area in contact with the snow?

3 Explain the following.

   a At a supermarket, cheese is cut into blocks using a metal wire.

   b Tanks move using caterpillar tracks instead of wheels.

Working out the pressure

How much pressure is needed to push a drawing pin into a board? How is it possible for a person to lie on a bed of nails? Why are stiletto heels banned from dance floors?

All these questions can be answered by working out the pressure caused by the force.

Two variables – force and area

If a drawing pin does not pierce the surface, you push it harder. You increase the force. If a knife does not cut, you sharpen it. You reduce the area. The pressure depends on both the size of the force and the area it acts over.

How much pressure?

Pressure is calculated using the equation

$$\text{pressure} = \frac{\text{force}}{\text{area}} \quad \text{or} \quad P = \frac{F}{A}$$

The example on the right shows how to work out the pressure. The force is measured in newtons (N) and the area in square metres (m^2). The pressure is in N/m^2 or pascal (Pa). Sometimes it is more convenient to use units of cm^2 or mm^2 to measure a small area. In this case the pressure is worked out in N/cm^2 or N/mm^2.

The elephant and its keeper

An elephant weighs 50 000 N and its keeper weighs 750 N. When they walk across grass one of them causes more damage than the other to the surface. Yes, you've guessed, it is the keeper who causes the most damage, not the elephant.

Ouch?

Example

A force of 1000 N pushes down on an area of 4 m^2. Calculate the pressure.

Answer

$$\text{pressure} = \frac{\text{force}}{\text{area}}$$

$$= \frac{100 \text{ N}}{4 \text{ m}^2}$$

$$= 25 \text{ Pa}$$

> ### Did You Know?
>
> The atmosphere exerts an enormous pressure, about 100 000 Pa at the Earth's surface.

---

1 Cross-country runners wear spikes on the soles of their running shoes.

a Explain why the runners wear spikes.

b The runners use different spikes for hard and soft ground. Suggest how the spikes might be different, and explain why different spikes are needed.

2 The area of an elephant's foot is about 1000 cm^2. The area of the keeper's shoe heel is about 50 cm^2.

a Calculate the pressure exerted by the elephant and by the elephant's keeper.

b Explain why the elephant's keeper damages the grass more.

3 A man who weighs 700 N lies on a bed of nails. There are 1000 blunt nails on the bed, and each nail has an area of 1 mm^2.

a Calculate the area of the nails in cm^2.

b Calculate the pressure on the man in N/cm^2.

c What pressure would be caused if the man accidentally sat on just one of the blunt nails?

Forces that turn

Forces can make things move. They can stop things that are moving. They can squash things and stretch them. They can also make things rotate or turn. Whenever you ride a bicycle, open a door, or turn on a tap, you are using a force to make an object turn round.

Turning forces help you ride a bicycle   *open a door*   *and turn on a tap*

Steering a bicycle

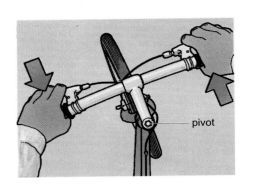

pivot

The diagram on the left shows how the handlebars move when a bicycle is steered towards the left. The central part of the handlebars does not change position, it only spins round. This part is called the **pivot**. The rest of the handlebars turn around the pivot.

To make the handlebars turn, you need a force. The force can be in any direction except directly towards or away from the pivot. A force directed towards the pivot does not cause any turning.

Tutning things around

To make an object turn round, you need two things. Firstly there has to be a pivot (also called an axis of rotation). When a wheel turns, the pivot is the axle at the centre. When a door opens, the pivot is the hinge.

The second thing you need is a force that is not directed towards or away from the pivot.

1 List six examples of forces being used to turn something.

2 The diagrams below show forces being used to turn things. The force and the pivot have been marked on one diagram. On copies of the other diagrams, label the force and the pivot.

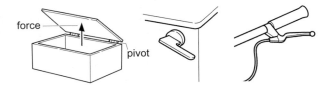

force

pivot

3 The diagram below is a plan view of a door. Three forces have been drawn.

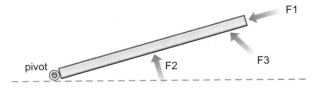

F1

pivot   F2   F3

a Which force cannot be used to open the door?

b Explain why this force will not open the door.

Magnifying the movement

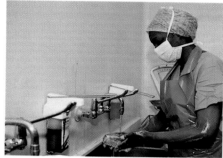

Some jobs can be made easier by changing the size of a force. Other jobs can be made easier by changing the distance that a force moves. A **lever** is a device that uses the turning effect of a force. It can make it easier to do a job by changing either the size of a force or the distance it moves.

A lever is not as complicated as it sounds. A simple bar of metal, wood, or plastic will often do the job. Taps and spanners are everyday examples of levers that magnify forces. Other levers magnify the distance moved by the force.

The lever on this tap makes it easy for the nurse to turn it with her elbow

Using tweezers

In a pair of tweezers, the pivot is at the end where the two prongs join. This part does not move. The prongs turn around this pivot. The ends that are furthest away move the greatest distance.

Your fingers move a small distance, called the **input movement**. The jaws move a much greater distance, called the **output movement**. This is how tweezers magnify movement.

Going fishing

A fishing rod is another example of a lever that magnifies movement. The pivot is the base of the rod, and one hand is usually placed close to the pivot. When this hand moves a small distance (the input movement), the far end of the rod moves a much greater distance (the output movement). The hand needs to exert a large force to move the rod. This force is much greater than the force that pulls the fish.

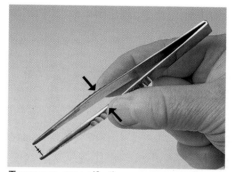

Tweezers magnify the movement of your fingers

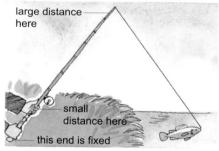

large distance here

small distance here

this end is fixed

A fishing rod magnifies the movement of your hand

1. What are the advantages of using a pair of tweezers to pick up small objects?

2. A fishing rod is a lever that magnifies movement.

   a Explain how a fishing rod makes it more convenient to catch fish.

   b Draw a diagram of a fishing rod. Label the pivot, the input movement, and the output movement.

3. a Write down three examples, not given on this page, of levers that magnify movement.

   b For each example, draw a diagram of the lever showing how it works. Label the pivot, the input movement, and the output movement.

Did You Know?

The gears on a bicycle magnify movement. Without gears, the bicycle is easy to pedal but the movement is slow. Before gears were invented, the penny farthing overcame the problem by having a large front wheel that was the driving wheel.

Magnifying the force

Sometimes the biggest force you can exert is not strong enough to do a straightforward task. You can use a machine to help you. Complex machines use electricity or another energy source, but there are many simple machines that rely on human power. They magnify the force that you exert.

Opening a tin (of beans or paint)

When you use a tin opener to open a baked bean tin, you first have to pierce the top of the tin. This requires a high pressure and a large force, larger than your hand can easily push with. The tin opener acts as a lever that multiplies the force. A small **input force** from your hand applied at the end of the handle is magnified. It exerts a larger **output force** on the tin lid closer to the pivot.

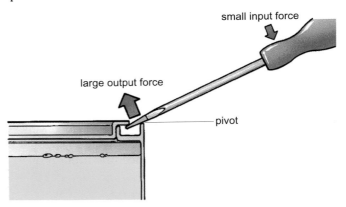

Tins of paint can also be difficult to open. You can use an old screwdriver to open a tin of paint. The pivot is the point on the blade that rests on the rim of the tin. As with the tin opener, a small input force applied far away from the pivot is magnified to a larger output force that acts close to the pivot. Everyday objects such as scissors, pincers, and taps all use levers to magnify forces.

This person is using pulleys to magnify his/her force

Did You Know?

The stones used to build the Egyptian pyramids each weigh around 2 tonnes. They were put in position without any energy source except people. The Egyptian workers used levers and pulley systems to magnify their forces.

 1 The diagram below shows a pair of scissors being used to cut some paper. On a copy of the diagram, label the pivot. Use arrows to show the size and direction of the input and output forces.

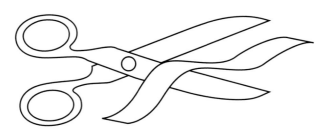

2 a Write down three examples, not given on this page, of levers that magnify force.

  b For each example, draw a diagram of the lever showing how it works. Label the pivot, the input force, and the output force.

3 A spanner magnifies a force to turn a nut or bolt.

  a Draw a diagram of a spanner being used, labelling the pivot, the input force, and the output force.

  b Spanners come in different lengths. What is the relationship between the length of the handle and the magnification of the force by the spanner?

To balance a seesaw, you do not always have to have equal forces on each side. In this experiment you will work out a rule for balancing a seesaw.

Instructions

1 Use a metre rule, pivoted on a wedge or with a screwdriver through a hole in the middle, and some 1 N weights.

2 For each diagram, you have to find the size of the unknown force that makes the seesaw balance. Record your results in a table.

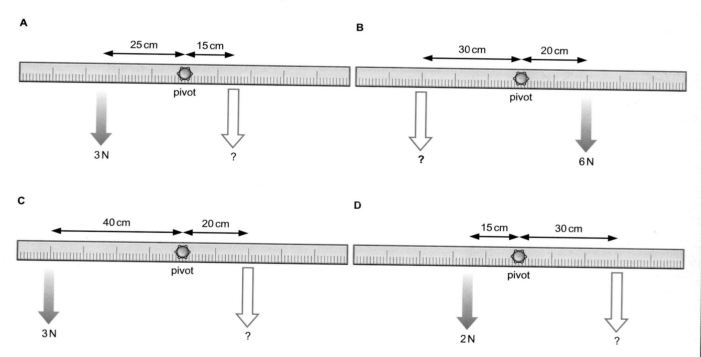

A

25 cm   15 cm

pivot

3 N   ?

B

30 cm   20 cm

pivot

?   6 N

C

40 cm   20 cm

pivot

3 N   ?

D

15 cm   30 cm

pivot

2 N   ?

What's the rule?

1 Use your results to write down a rule for balancing a seesaw. Your rule should use scientific words such as **force** and **distance**.

Checking the rule

1 You have to balance a 4 N weight on one side of the seesaw with a 2 N weight on the other side. Make a prediction about the distances of the 4 N weight and the 2 N weight from the pivot.

2 Test your prediction by finding four different sets of distances for the weights to balance. Put your results in a table.

3 Now do the same for a 4 N weight and a 6 N weight.

Balanced seesaws

This bridge is designed so that it does not tip over, no matter what the load is

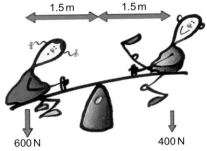

The moment of the girl's force is 600 N × 1.5 m = 900 N m, and the moment of the boy's force is 400 N × 1.5 m = 600 N m

---

Example

The girl's moment is 900 N m anticlockwise. At what distance from the pivot will the boy's moment balance the girl's moment?

moment = force × distance
= 900 N m

900 N m = 400 N × distance

$$\text{distance} = \frac{900 \text{ N m}}{400 \text{ N}} = 2.25 \text{ m}$$

So the boy sits 2.25 m from the pivot to balance the seesaw.

Did You Know?

A mechanic uses a tool called a torque wrench to measure the moment applied when tightening a nut.

Balancing a seesaw is not just something that happens in a playground! Engineers and designers need to understand how to balance a seesaw so that they can produce goods and buildings that are safe.

Moving along the seesaw

In what way should the boy in the diagram move to balance the seesaw? Because he exerts a smaller force on the seesaw than the girl does, he needs to sit further away from the pivot. His turning effect on the seesaw depends on two factors: the **force** and its **distance** from the pivot. The turning effect of a force is called its **moment**. You can calculate the moment of a force using the following equation. The moment of a force has the unit newton metres, N m.

moment = force × shortest distance from the force line to the pivot

The seesaw tips with the girl's end down because the (anticlockwise) moment of the girl's force is bigger than the (clockwise) moment of the boy's force.

Balancing the seesaw

For the seesaw to balance, the moments must be balanced. This means that the clockwise moment is balanced by an equal-sized anticlockwise moment. The boy could balance the seesaw by moving so that he is 2.25 m from the pivot. The example on the left shows how to work this out. His moment would then be equal in size to the girl's moment, with the turning effect acting in the opposite direction.

1 a Explain how a change in the girl's position instead of the boy's could balance the seesaw.

   b Where does she need to sit for the seesaw to be balanced?

2 Calculate the force required to balance each seesaw below.

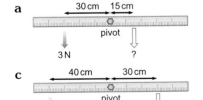

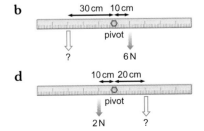

3 a A 4 N weight on one side of a seesaw is to be balanced with a 2 N weight on the other side. Write down the relationship between the distance from each weight to the pivot.

   b Do the same for a 4 N weight and a 6 N weight.

Stability

Why are bowling pins easy to knock over while traffic cones stay upright? The difference is to do with the turning effect of the weight force when they are tipped. Traffic cones are **stable**, while bowling pins are **unstable**.

Designing a traffic cone

There are two features about the shape of a traffic cone that make it stable.

1 Most of the mass is in the bottom half of the cone. In a shape like this, the weight force that pulls the cone down acts from a point low down on the cone.

2 The cone has a wide base. This means that when the cone is tipped, it falls back on its base instead of falling over.

The diagram on the right shows a cone that has been tipped. The edge of the cone acts as a pivot. The weight of the cone has a turning effect around that point. As long as the weight arrow falls inside the base, the cone falls back upright. It will only topple if the line of this arrow passes outside the cone's base. You would have to tip the cone a long way for this to happen.

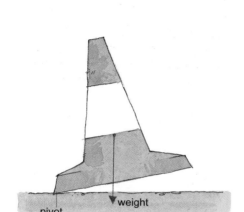

Knocking the pins down

When you go bowling, the pins topple easily when the ball hits them. There are two main reasons for this.

1 The bowling pin has more mass in its top half than the traffic cone does, so the weight force acts from a point higher up the pin.

2 The pin has a narrow base. When the pin is tipped, it falls over instead of going back upright onto its base.

The diagram on the right shows what happens when a bowling pin is tipped by the same amount as the traffic cone. Because the weight force acts from higher up and the base is narrower, the weight arrow falls outside the base. This means that the weight of the pin has a turning effect that makes the pin fall over.

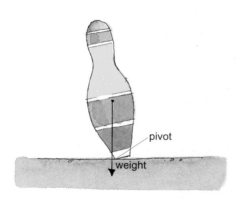

1 What two factors determine whether an object is stable or unstable?

2 On a double-decker bus, passengers are allowed to stand on the lower deck but standing is not allowed on the upper deck. Explain why.

3 Use diagrams to explain which is more stable when filled with water, a measuring cylinder or a conical flask.

Did You Know?

A half-full bottle of milk is more stable than either an empty bottle or a full bottle.

Skeletons in the cupboard

Skeletons for support, protection, and movement

The main job of a skeleton is to support the organism. Wherever you live, you need to be supported against the pull of gravity (your weight). This is especially true for organisms that live on land. In water you weigh less because the water helps to support you. Organisms that live in water need less support from their skeletons.

There are two other jobs that skeletons do. One is protection. A hard skeleton can cover delicate soft parts to prevent them being damaged (eg your skull covers your brain). The other job is helping with movement. A skeleton provides a firm anchor for muscles to pull on.

Even cells have skeletons. Inside them are tiny tubes called **microtubules**. These help keep the cell in shape, and help it to move.

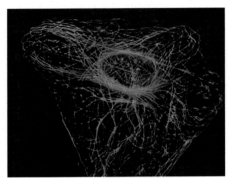

This cell has been magnified by a microscope. You can see the skeleton of microtubules which support it.

Skeletons in plants

Bigger organisms have evolved special tissues for support. Plants have woody tissues such as xylem to support them. Water pressure also helps to keep them firm and upright. You may have seen a wilted plant. It has flopped because it is short of water pressure.

The plant wilts because it is short of water. After it has been watered, water pressure holds it upright.

Skeletons in animals

Many animals also use water pressure for support. Jellyfish and earthworms are two examples. Animals may also have special support tissues. Crabs and insects (arthropods) have an outer skeleton that fits outside the body like a suit of armour. This contains a chemical called chitin (pronounced kite-in). Molluscs such as snails have a shell made from calcium carbonate. Vertebrates, including ourselves, have evolved bones for support.

Did You Know?

What do you think of when you hear the word skeleton? Bones? Most living things have a skeleton, but only some of them have bones.

A crab has a skeleton containing chitin that surrounds its body

What Do You Think?

If crabs are surrounded by a hard skeleton, how do they get bigger?

1 What are the three functions of a skeleton?

2 In what two ways do plants support themselves?

3 What special substances are used in the skeletons of animals?

You and your skeleton

Mainly bone

Your own skeleton is made mostly of bone, along with a material called cartilage. Cartilage is softer than bone. The diagram shows your skeleton.

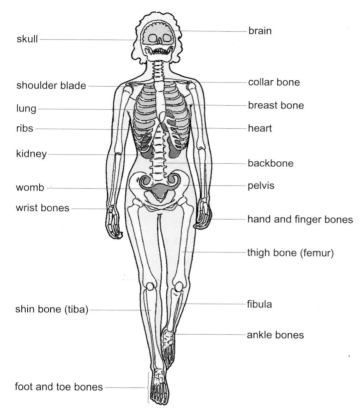

skull — brain
shoulder blade — collar bone
lung — breast bone
ribs — heart
kidney — backbone
womb — pelvis
wrist bones — hand and finger bones
— thigh bone (femur)
shin bone (tiba) — fibula
— ankle bones
foot and toe bones

Your skeleton supports and protects your body

Your skeleton has four main parts.

1 Your skull surrounds and protects your brain.
2 Your spine (backbone) supports your body. It is made of lots of small bones called vertebrae. These move over each other so that you can bend some ways but not others.
3 Your ribs support your chest. They surround and protect your heart and lungs. They also help you to breathe.
4 Your limbs are your arms and legs. They are jointed to allow you to walk and carry things. The legs also support your weight.

 1 What materials is your skeleton made of?

2 How does your spine bend?

3 Name three parts of the human skeleton that protect delicate organs.

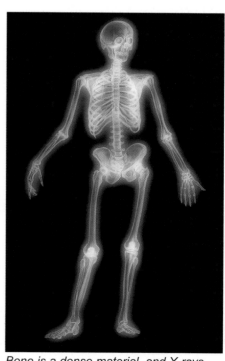

Bone is a dense material, and X-rays cannot pass through it. Bone makes a shadow on an X-ray picture. This X-ray picture shows the whole body.

51

Moving about

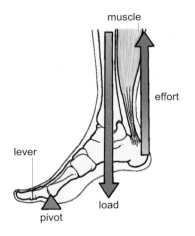

Joints

One of the most obvious features of most animals is that they move about. This means that they cannot have a totally fixed skeleton. Imagine being welded into a suit of armour! Animals have solved this problem by having joints in their skeletons. In vertebrates there are five types of moving joint. There are seesaw joints; wheelbarrow joints; hinge joints; ball and socket joints, and gliding joints.

Joints act as lever systems that are an aid to movement. Muscles are attached to the bones and pull on them. As they move, the bones also move all the organs they support. The joints may have to support a lot of weight or they may need to allow fine movements to occur. The type of joint used at any part of the skeleton will depend on the forces around it.

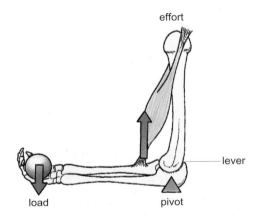

Lifting the body

The ankle has to support the weight of the body. You want to use as little energy as possible for this so the joint system needs to be an efficient lever to reduce the energy use. In the ankle system the pivot is at one end and the effort for lifting is at the other. The weight is in the middle. The result of this set-up is that a small effort by the muscles can raise the large force created by the body's mass. This is how a wheelbarrow works to help you move heavy loads.

Flexibilty

In the arm it is important for the hand to have a good range of movement rather than to be able to carry heavy weights. This means the joint system does not have to be so energy-efficient. Try holding some books on your hands with the elbows bent. The muscles soon tire. The mass of the books acts along the length of the forearm creating a large force. The muscle pulls from near the elbow and acts over a much shorter distance. To generate the same force takes a lot of energy. However, the shape of the system allows you to reach over your shoulder to scratch your back.

> **What Do You Think?**
>
> Why haven't animals evolved wheels?

---

1. Explain why animals need joints.

2. What are the main types of moving joints in vertebrates?

3. How do the joints under the head work? What sort of lever system are they?

4. How do ball and socket joints work? What problems do they pose?

Muscle power

Muscles getting shorter

The joints in your skeleton allow you to move, but it is your muscles that supply the force when you move. Muscle cells are long and thin and join together to form fibres. The fibres are held together in bundles. The bundles are grouped together and wrapped in a sheath. This is what we call a muscle. Inside the muscle cells are special proteins which can move over each other. When they move, the muscle gets shorter or **contracts**. Muscles use energy to contract.

Antagonistic muscle pairs

Muscles cannot get longer again of their own accord. They need to be pulled back to their original length when they are relaxed. This is done by another muscle working in the opposite direction. Muscles are therefore arranged in pairs or opposite sets. Each muscle in the pair has the opposite effect when it contracts. These pairs or sets are called **antagonistic** muscles.

In the upper arm there is a pair of antagonistic muscles called the **biceps** and the **triceps**. To lift the lower arm towards the shoulder, the biceps contracts and the triceps is stretched. To lower the arm again, the triceps contracts and the biceps is stretched. To allow for graded movements, both muscles usually work together with one pulling more than the other.

Antagonistic muscles in the gut

Even in your gut there are antagonistic muscles. The **circular muscles** run around the tube that forms the gut. When they contract, the gut gets longer and thinner. The **longitudinal muscles** run along the length of the tube. When they contract, the gut gets shorter and wider. Working together, these muscles make waves that squeeze the food along. This movement is called **peristalsis**. It can happen in all muscular tubes in animals.

> ### Did You Know?
>
> If all your muscles contracted at once, you could crush your bones!

?

1 Explain carefully how a muscle contracts.

2 What is meant by antagonistic muscles?

3 Draw a series of labelled diagrams to show how peristalsis pushes food along the gut.

4 Earthworms have a skeleton supported by water pressure. Find out how they use antagonistic muscles to move.

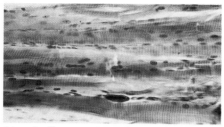

Muscle fibres seen under a microscope. When the long muscle fibres shorten, the muscle contracts and pulls on a bone.

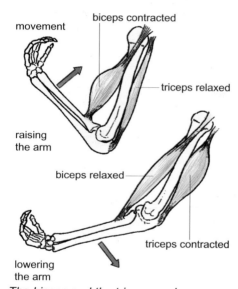

movement

biceps contracted

triceps relaxed

raising the arm

biceps relaxed

triceps contracted

lowering the arm

The biceps and the triceps work together to control the movement of the lower arm

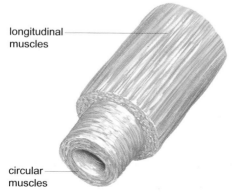

longitudinal muscles

circular muscles

The circular muscles and the longitudinal muscles work together to move food along the gut

Lung power

In your body, your cells respire glucose to release energy. This process uses oxygen and produces carbon dioxide. You get the oxygen for respiration from the air around you. You give out the carbon dioxide into the air. This exchange of gases happens in your lungs. The lungs form one of the body's main transport systems. Oxygen passes from the air into the blood, and carbon dioxide passes out of the blood into the air.

The lining of the bronchus magnified ×4000 times by a microscope. The worm-like threads are the cilia which move mucus up and away from the lungs.

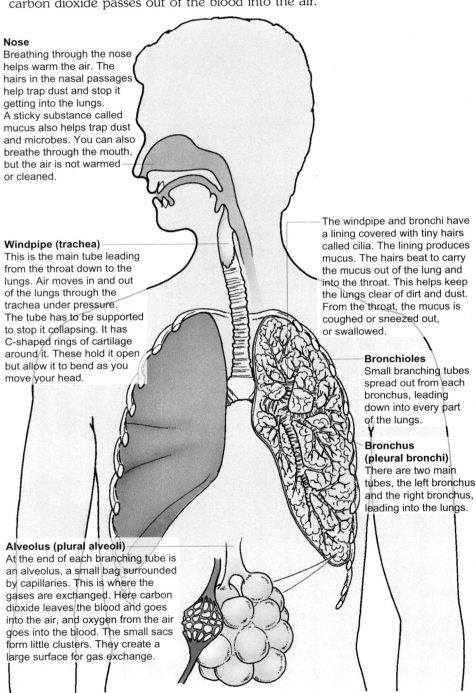

Nose
Breathing through the nose helps warm the air. The hairs in the nasal passages help trap dust and stop it getting into the lungs. A sticky substance called mucus also helps trap dust and microbes. You can also breathe through the mouth, but the air is not warmed or cleaned.

Windpipe (trachea)
This is the main tube leading from the throat down to the lungs. Air moves in and out of the lungs through the trachea under pressure. The tube has to be supported to stop it collapsing. It has C-shaped rings of cartilage around it. These hold it open but allow it to bend as you move your head.

The windpipe and bronchi have a lining covered with tiny hairs called cilia. The lining produces mucus. The hairs beat to carry the mucus out of the lung and into the throat. This helps keep the lungs clear of dirt and dust. From the throat, the mucus is coughed or sneezed out, or swallowed.

Bronchioles
Small branching tubes spread out from each bronchus, leading down into every part of the lungs.

Bronchus (pleural bronchi)
There are two main tubes, the left bronchus and the right bronchus, leading into the lungs.

Alveolus (plural alveoli)
At the end of each branching tube is an alveolus, a small bag surrounded by capillaries. This is where the gases are exchanged. Here carbon dioxide leaves the blood and goes into the air, and oxygen from the air goes into the blood. The small sacs form little clusters. They create a large surface for gas exchange.

?

1 What prevents the tubes in the lungs collapsing?

2 What stops dust and dirt getting into the lungs?

3 Explain what happens in the alveoli.

4 Why is it better to breathe through your nose than your mouth?

5 What happens to the oxygen after it goes into your blood in the alveoli?

Deep breathing

The lungs are surrounded by two membranes called the pleura. Underneath the lungs is a tough sheet called the **diaphragm** (pronounced die-a-fram). This completely separates the chest from the abdomen. The membranes and the diaphragm make the chest an airtight system.

Breathing in and out

When you breathe in, you make the chest cavity bigger. Your ribs rise up and your diaphragm moves down and flattens. You can feel this happen if you place your fingertips just under your breast bone. Because the chest cavity has got bigger, the air pressure inside the chest is lower than the air pressure of the atmosphere. Air is forced in through the nose (and mouth if it is open) by the difference in air pressure.

When you breathe out, the reverse happens. The ribs move down (mostly under their own weight) and the diaphragm domes upwards. The chest cavity gets smaller. The air pressure inside it is now higher than the pressure of the atmosphere. Air is forced out of the lungs through the nose and mouth.

Tidal air

The air moved in and out of the lungs during breathing is called **tidal air**, because it goes in and out like the tide! Tidal movements change some of the air in the lungs each time you breathe. Some air stays in the lungs even after you have breathed out. This air is not changed each time you breathe. It mixes with the tidal air by diffusion.

The amount of tidal air changes depending on how deeply you breathe. At rest you only change about 10% of your lung volume each breath. After heavy exercise you may change as much as 75% each breath.

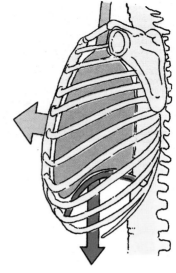

air forced in

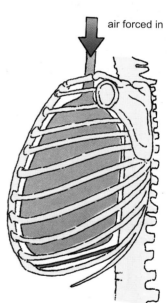

ribs raised, diaphragm flattened

When you breathe in, your chest cavity expands and air is forced in

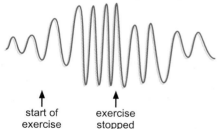

↑ start of exercise   ↑ exercise stopped

This trace records how quickly and how deeply someone breathed before, during, and after exercise

1. Explain how you breathe in.

2. Draw a sequence of diagrams to show what happens when you breathe out.

3. Why can you never move all of the air in the lungs when you breathe?

4. a What makes the chest airtight?

   b Why is this important?

Did You Know?

Most people breathe in and out about 16 times per minute. That makes about 23 040 breaths in a day. How many in a year?

Smoking and health

Starting to smoke is usually a social activity. It can lead to a habit lasting a lifetime.

What does smoking do to you?

Cigarettes contain nicotine, an addictive drug. Smoking cigarettes can be a calming activity. It makes people feel relaxed. It can make you feel sick. Although people feel relaxed, nicotine is making their heart beat faster. It also affects how your nerves work by changing their chemistry. If you start smoking, it is very difficult to give it up. Everyone knows that smoking is bad for you. So why do people start to smoke in the first place?

Why do people smoke?

People start smoking for social reasons. Some people do it to rebel. Some start because they have friends who already smoke. Some think it makes them look grown up. In most cases people start smoking as part of a social group.

The health risks of smoking

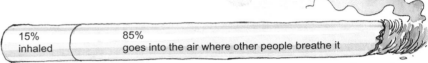

| 15% inhaled | 85% goes into the air where other people breathe it |

Tobacco smoke contains over 400 chemicals. At least 60 of them are known to cause cancer.

On its own, nicotine is not particularly harmful. However, as well as nicotine, cigarette smoke contains hundreds of poisonous chemicals. Many of these cause cancer. Regular smoking makes it 20 times more likely that you will get lung cancer. Smoking also makes you produce more stomach acid. This is likely to give you ulcers and stomach cancer. Smoking also damages your heart and blood vessels. Smokers are more likely to die of a heart attack or stroke than non-smokers.

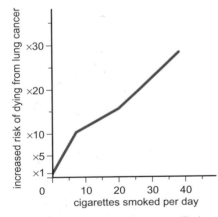

The more you smoke, the more likely you are to die of cancer. Smoking also makes you more likely to die of heart disease. Smoking cigars or a pipe also causes cancer and heart disease.

Passive smoking

There is now evidence that breathing other people's cigarette smoke also increases your risk of cancer. This is called **passive smoking**. As a result, smoking has been banned in many public places.

Did You Know?

Sir Walter Raleigh first brought tobacco back from America. He found you could smoke it in a pipe. He learnt this from native Americans. There is a story that his servant threw a bucket of water over him, thinking his master was on fire. Despite this, tobacco smoking soon caught on.

1 Where did Sir Walter Raleigh discover tobacco?

2 What is the main factor in starting smoking?

3 Why do people carry on smoking?

4 Make a list of reasons why smoking should be banned in public places. Make another list of reasons why it should not be banned.

5 What other effects of smoking can you think of?

Producing carbon dioxide

Mammals are not the only animals that exchange gases. Insects have a special system of tubes called tracheae (pronounced track-ee-ee). Through these tubes they take in oxygen from the air and give out carbon dioxide, as we do. You can show that carbon dioxide is produced using hydrogencarbonate indicator. This indicator is very sensitive to changes in acidity. Carbon dioxide dissolves to form a weak acid, which turns the indicator yellow.

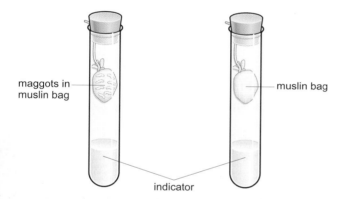

maggots in muslin bag

muslin bag

indicator

Instructions

1 Put some hydrogencarbonate indicator into a clean test tube.

2 Wrap some maggots in a small muslin bag.

3 Hang the bag in the tube without letting it touch the indicator.

4 Set up another tube but without the maggots.

5 Leave the experiment for about 30 minutes.

6 What happens to the indicator? What does this tell you?

Gas exchange

It is also possible to measure how much gas is exchanged by animals in a simple way. The next experiment shows you how.

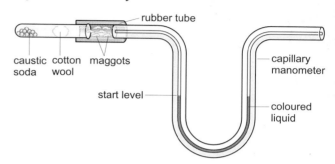

rubber tube

caustic soda   cotton wool   maggots

start level

capillary manometer

coloured liquid

WARNING

Wear safety goggles

Caustic soda will burn your skin if you get it on yourself.

Instructions

1 Take a small test tube and put some caustic soda in the bottom.

2 Push some cotton wool into the test tube until it is just above the caustic soda.

3 Attach a rubber tube to the end of the test tube. Place some maggots in the rubber tube.

4 Attach a capillary manometer to the end as shown. Make sure there is some coloured water in the 'U' tube.

5 Mark the level of the water. Leave the maggots for an hour (or a measured period of time) and then mark the level again. What has happened to it?

6 The volume of oxygen taken in by the maggots is very nearly the same as the volume of carbon dioxide given out. Caustic soda absorbs carbon dioxide. Given these two facts, can you explain why the apparatus gives us a good measure of the amount of gases exchanged by the maggots?

Microbes

Microbes are tiny living things. They are so small that we can only see them with a microscope. Microbes include bacteria, viruses, some single-celled organisms called protists, and some fungi.

Bacteria

Bacteria are simple cells. They do not have a nucleus. Their genetic material is in a simple loop of DNA. Bacteria can transfer DNA from one bacterium to another. This means bacteria can change very rapidly. This helps them adapt to changes around them. They can also reproduce very quickly. In the right conditions a bacterium can divide into two cells every 30 minutes.

Viruses

Viruses are even simpler. They have no cytoplasm as cells do. They are just a box of protein with either some DNA or some RNA inside. They only reproduce inside living cells. They take over the cell they have invaded and make it produce more viruses. Many scientists think viruses are not really alive. They have probably evolved from living things, because they use the same genetic code. Like bacteria, virus DNA changes easily and so viruses also keep changing and adapting.

<blockquote>
Did You Know?

*The microbe is so very small,
you cannot make him out at all,
But many sanguine people hope
to see him through a microscope.*

The poet Hilaire Belloc wrote this when scientists did not know much about microbes. 'Sanguine' means hopeful, and the scientists did later see microbes.
</blockquote>

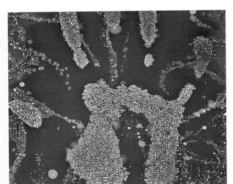

These bacteria have grown from the imprint of a human hand pressed into agar. Bacteria are some of the smallest living things.

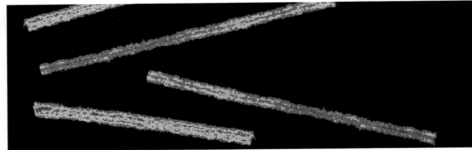

Viruses are even smaller than bacteria. These are tobacco mosaic viruses. They look like regularly shaped boxes of protein.

Useful microbes

Most people think microbes cause diseases. Many of them do cause illnesses, not only in people, but in other animals and in plants. However, many microbes are very useful. Microbes in the soil help recycle nutrients that are needed by living things. We use similar microbes in sewage treatment. We use yeast and other microbes which can make useful things like bread, wine, and antibiotics.

 1 Name four types of organism that are called microbes.

2 How are bacteria able to change their DNA rapidly?

 3 Explain how viruses reproduce.

4 Research as many different uses of microbes as you can.

You can grow microbes in the laboratory. All you need to do is supply them with some food, water, and warmth. One way to do this is to grow them on a jelly made from seaweed. This jelly, called **agar**, has had nutrients added to it. The agar is dissolved in water. It is left to set in the bottom of a Petri dish and the dish of agar is called an agar plate. You can see any microbe colonies that grow on the surface of the agar quite easily.

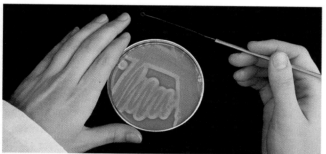

Microbes grow in groups called colonies, which you can see on this agar plate

When working with microbes it is important to keep everything very clean. Microbes from the air or the bench or your skin can easily get onto the agar when the lid is open. You do not want just any microbes getting into the plates. You want to see the microbes that you have put there to grow. Make sure that you have everything you need beside you before opening a plate. Only open the plate for the shortest possible time. Never breathe on the plate when it is open.

Once you have made the plate, seal it and label it. The label should give the date, what has been done to the plate, and your name. Stick the label to the bottom of the plate so you will always know what is on the jelly.

> ### WARNING
> Once you have sealed agar plates do not reopen them.

Instructions

1 Take five fresh, sterile agar plates. Label them **1** to **5**.

2 Leave plate **1** unopened.

3 Open plate **2** and place it on a shelf away from people for 2 minutes. Then close it up.

4 Open plate **3** and rinse a little tap water over the surface very quickly. Pour the water away and quickly shut the plate.

5 Do the same with plate **4** but use pond water.

6 Wash your hands and dry them. Open plate **5** and quickly but gently touch the agar. Close the plate.

7 Seal each plate. Complete the labels with your name, the date, and what you did to each.

8 Leave the plates in a warm place for a few days to let the microbes grow.

9 Which plates have produced colonies? Draw any colonies that have grown.

10 What can you say about where microbes are found?

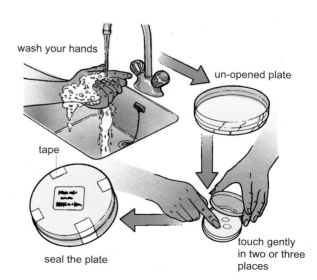

wash your hands

un-opened plate

tape

seal the plate

touch gently in two or three places

Under attack

Disease	Caused by (type of microbe)
chickenpox	virus
common cold	viruses
dysentery	protist
'flu (influenza)	viruses
malaria	protist
measles	virus
tetanus (lockjaw)	bacterium
tuberculosis (TB)	bacterium

Some common diseases and the microbes that cause them

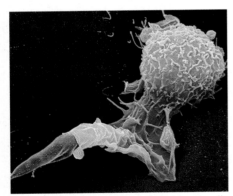

This photograph shows white blood cells killing and eating bacteria

A place for microbes to live

Your body is large and warm. It contains food and water. It is an ideal place for microbes to live in! Some microbes live inside us and do us no harm. You have microbes in your gut which help you digest food. However, many of the microbes that try to live in us cause damage to our cells. They may eat the cells, or use them to make more microbes. They may produce poisons which harm the cells. When your cells are damaged, you get ill.

How the microbes get in

Microbes can enter your body in a number of ways. Your nose, mouth, eyes, ears, anus, bladder, and sex organs all connect the inside of your body to the outside world. A cut or scratch also allows microbes in from the outside. Your body has to have good defences or you would always be ill.

First line defences

First line defences try to prevent microbes getting into your body. Your nose and airways produce sticky mucus to trap dust and microbes. Cilia move the mucus and microbes back out of your body. Your ears produce wax to protect the ear canals. Tears in your eyes and the oil on your skin kill microbes. Any microbes that you swallow enter your stomach, which is very acidic. The acid kills most bacteria. Cuts in your skin are quickly covered by a scab.

Second line defences

You have two second line defences to deal with invading microbes. You have an army of white blood cells which kill and eat microbes. White blood cells are made in special glands in the lymph system, called lymph nodes. The white blood cells produce **antibodies**, special proteins that fight the microbes. You also produce interferon which neutralizes viruses.

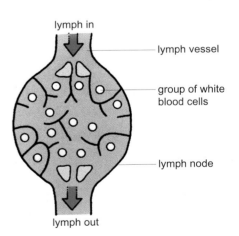

lymph in
lymph vessel
group of white blood cells
lymph node
lymph out

1. How can microbes damage cells?
2. Explain four ways in which your body prevents microbes getting in.
3. What are the body's second line defences?
4. Draw an outline human body and label it to show where microbes can get in.

Medicine fights back

Sanitation – a clean water supply

Apart from the body's defences, people have found other ways to fight diseases. Microbes spread in a number of ways. Many microbes are spread through water supplies. Cleaning the water supply breaks the infection cycle.

Vaccination

One of the world's worst diseases was smallpox. Most people who got smallpox died. The Chinese were the first to discover a way to protect healthy people. They took powdered scabs from a smallpox sufferer and inhaled them. This made people **immune** to the disease. The process was developed by the Arabs and introduced in Europe in about 1700. Dr Edward Jenner developed the process of vaccination in Britain. Today we are protected against many diseases by vaccination.

A doctor or nurse injects a **vaccine**. This is an inactive or only very mildly active form of the organism causing disease. Your body responds by producing antibodies in the blood which attack the vaccine. These antibodies remain to protect you from further attack for several years.

Medicines

People throughout the world have always used plant and animal products as medicines. The chemical in aspirin tablets (salicylic acid) is found in many plants. Drugs work in all kinds of ways. Some drugs relieve the symptoms, helping people rest free from pain. They do not treat the cause of the disease. Others, such as antibiotics, kill microbes (such as bacteria, protists, and fungi) in your body. Antibiotics do not affect viruses.

Because microbes can change their DNA rapidly, many are now resistant to antibiotics. So-called 'superbugs' have appeared that are not killed off by most antibiotics.

Antiseptics and disinfectants

People have also invented chemicals to keep their surroundings clean. Antiseptics and disinfectants kill microbes. They can be used to wipe over surfaces where we prepare food, or where we treat ill people.

What Do You Think?

Smallpox only exists locked up in research laboratories. The virus is extinct in the wild. Do you think it should be destroyed completely?

The modern pharmaceutical industry produces a wide range of medicines to treat all sorts of diseases

We use antiseptics on ourselves, and disinfectants on surfaces and other things, to kill microbes and stop diseases spreading

1. Explain how vaccination works.

2. Why do you think clean water can be more important in fighting disease than antibiotics?

3. Antiseptics and a clean water supply work in a similar way to fight disease. Explain this.

4. Drugs need careful testing before being used on people. Do you think it is right to use animals for these tests?

5. Find out the recommended sequence of vaccinations for children in Great Britain.

Staying healthy

This 'clear' artery will become 'clogged' by eating too much fatty food

Eating disorders

Apart from diseases caused by microbes, we can get ill in other ways. If you eat too much, you become **obese** (fat). The extra weight can strain your heart and damage your joints. If you eat too little you become **malnourished**. **Anorexia** is an illness that makes people so worried about being fat that they eat very little. They may even make themselves sick after meals. The illness is a mental disorder, but it can kill.

Eating too much of certain foods can also harm you. If you eat food containing lots of cholesterol (a sort of fat), your arteries may become narrowed and blocked. The coronary arteries take blood to the heart. If these arteries become blocked the heart muscle has no oxygen and stops working (seizes). This is a **heart attack**. Narrowing of the arteries also raises the blood pressure. This may cause blood vessels to burst. If this happens in the brain it damages some of the brain tissue. This is a **stroke**. Heart attacks and strokes kill many people in the UK each year.

To lift up a heavy weight, you should bend at the knees and keep your back as straight as possible

Bad posture

Sitting or standing in an unbalanced position (bad posture) can damage your joints. Many people suffer from back trouble. This is often caused by poor posture. It can also be due to lifting heavy weights without bending at the knees. This sort of damage can be permanent and very painful.

Regular exercise helps keep your muscles and joints healthy. It improves your posture. It also exercises your heart and lungs, and makes you feel more alert.

Preventing (these) illnesses

There are two ways by which you can help yourself stay healthy: maintain a balanced diet; take regular exercise. Together, these will reduce the risk associated with eating disorders and bad posture.

Regular exercise makes you fitter, stronger, and more supple

1 What can happen to you if you eat too much food?

2 a What is a heart attack?

   b What makes a heart attack more likely?

3 Describe how someone should lift a heavy weight from the floor to a table.

4 What are the benefits of regular exercise?

Drinking alcohol

Alcoholic drinks have been made by most human cultures. If alcohol was discovered today it would almost certainly be banned. Alcohol is a depressant drug. It slows down the body chemistry and affects the nervous system. People may say that drinking cheers them up and makes them lively. This is because alcohol affects the brain very quickly. It turns off some of their control mechanisms and they become less inhibited. It also relaxes their muscles.

An addictive drug

If people did not drink beyond the stage where they felt pleasantly relaxed, there would be no need to worry. However, alcohol is addictive. The more people drink, the more they need to drink to have the same effect. Constant use of alcohol damages the gut, the liver, and the brain. These effects take a long time to build up, but can eventually kill. Regular heavy drinking is one of the main causes of death in Britain. It is also a major factor in divorce, crime, and road accidents.

Many young people drink only occasionally but then they drink a lot (binge) at one time. This is as dangerous as drinking regularly. People who binge drink are more likely to die in an accident, or by choking on their own vomit.

How many units?

To check on how much people drink, they should work out how many units of alcohol they have. One unit is found in half a pint of beer, a glass of wine, or a pub measure of spirits. The recommendation for men is below 28 units a week and for women below 21 units a week.

Each of these drinks contains a unit of alcohol

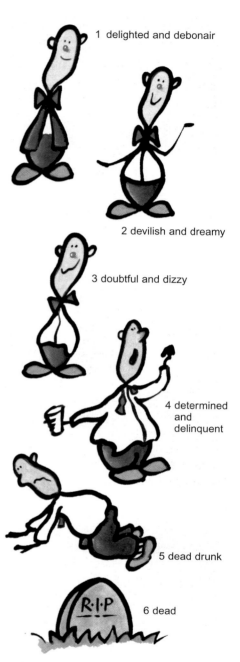

1 delighted and debonair

2 devilish and dreamy

3 doubtful and dizzy

4 determined and delinquent

5 dead drunk

6 dead

The six stages of drunkenness

 1 a What makes alcohol a dangerous drug?

   b What long-term effects does it have?

2 Why do people drink alcohol?

3 How many units of alcohol are there in three pints of beer and four measures of whisky?

Did You Know?

Around 800 people die each year in Britain because of people driving after drinking alcohol.

Drugs in society

All human societies use drugs! This statement is not meant to encourage people to use drugs. It should, however, make you stop and think. Why do humans use drugs? A **drug** is a difficult thing to define. What people usually mean is something illegal. Alcohol, nicotine, Aspirin and Paracetamol are all drugs and are all legal. The normal meaning of the word is, a potentially dangerous chemical, taken in, to change our mood or perceptions. The last aspect gives a clue to why people use drugs. The desire to change your mood or perception may be for medical reasons or simply for pleasure.

Gin drinking was a social problem in cities in Victorian times

A society's *legal* drugs

There have been several cultures in the world whose main legal drug has been cannabis. Mostly, though, people have used alcohol as their main legal drug. This has led to many social institutions and conventions being developed around the use of the drug. In Britain the development of pubs provides an interesting history of how alcohol use is controlled by society.

A society's *illegal* drugs

Illegal drugs also have social conventions surrounding their use. This often involves an element of danger which can make the taking of the drug seem more exciting and pleasurable. Whatever you do you should know that all drugs, legal or otherwise have side effects. They are all capable of harming you in some way. Illegal drugs are more likely to do this because of the circumstances in which they are obtained.

Soft or hard?

There are many so-called soft drugs, such as ecstasy or cannabis, which are likely to be offered to young people at parties or other social events. Hard drugs such as heroin and cocaine, are very addictive and cause major chemical upset to the body very quickly. Young children are more likely to suffer severe effects due to small body size. It may be hard to say no to these offers. One way to help yourself is to understand what the drugs can do and to realise the dangers to your health.

What Do You Think?

Over 250 000 people take prescribed tranquillizers, and many of them are addicted. Should tranquillizers be made illegal?

Ecstasy tablets, cannabis (above), and poppers are all illegal drugs. There is no control over how they are produced and sold, so you have no idea what you are taking if you accept a drug like this.

Did You Know?

Ecstasy upsets the water balance of the body, and can cause dehydration and death. Researchers think it also causes brain damage over a period of time.

1 What is meant by the word drug?

2 Why do you think all societies have some legal drugs?

3 Find out about the effects and dangers of ecstasy, glue-sniffing, and poppers.

4 Some people argue that the best way to control drug use is to make all drugs legal. Make a list of arguments in favour of this idea, and another list of arguments against it.

World health

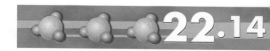

Health problems vary in different parts of the world. Poor health is linked to poverty in many countries. In other countries, poor health is linked to a lifestyle of plenty.

Infectious diseases and poverty

In countries where there is great poverty there is also often warfare and famine. This results in malnutrition, which makes people more likely to catch infectious diseases as well. In poor regions, there may not be clean water and proper sanitation. This leads to many deaths from diseases carried in the water. The pie chart shows the world's ten groups of killing infectious diseases. The majority of these are more common in poorer countries, or are bigger problems in poorer countries. AIDS is a deadly disease that we are all aware of in Europe, but the people in Africa are even more at risk from this disease.

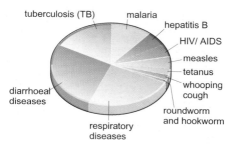

The ten groups of infectious diseases that kill most people worldwide

Overindulgence and affluence

By contrast, the biggest killing diseases in the developed countries are linked with a rich lifestyle. Cancer of the lungs kills 32 000 people in Britain each year, often caused by smoking. Many people have heart and circulatory problems caused by a rich diet high in saturated fat. The bar chart shows what kinds of diseases cause death in rich and poor countries.

Health care

An important factor in world health is the type of health care being provided. A great deal of money is spent on hospital services. Hospitals treat people who have already become ill. Very little money is spent on preventing people becoming ill in the first place. This would be a better and more cost-effective approach in many cases.

Recently many poor countries have had financial problems as banks have cut back loans and demanded repayments. These poor countries have had to reduce their spending, often cutting health budgets. In many cases, spending on weapons continues unchecked.

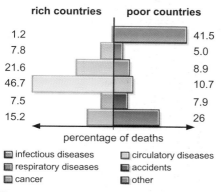

The causes of death in rich and poor countries

1 How does poverty lead to ill health?

2 Which of the infectious diseases shown in the pie chart do you think are transmitted by water?

3 What leads to poor health in rich countries?

4 Why do you think that some developing countries spend money on weapons rather than health care?

Did You Know?

Children who have measles in Britain become ill but are unlikely to die. In some developing countries, health care and hygiene are not so good and measles kills as many people as AIDS does.

23.01

ACIDS, BASES, AND SALTS

The acid in a lemon turns blue litmus paper red

Hydrochloric acid reacts with calcium carbonate to form carbon dioxide gas

Hydrochloric acid reacts with magnesium to form hydrogen gas

Did You Know?

Milk contains a sugar called lactose. When milk is left in a warm place it goes sour. Bacteria turn the lactose into an acid called lactic acid.

Common acids

Many substances around us contain **acids**. Lemon juice, vinegar, and cooking apples taste sour. They all contain acids, which give the sour taste. These acids are all natural or **organic acids**.

Mineral acids

You use other acids in the laboratory. These include hydrochloric acid, sulphuric acid, and nitric acid. These acids are usually made from materials in the Earth or the air. They are called **mineral acids**. As well as being used for experiments, mineral acids are used in industry to make many different products. Sulphuric acid is used in car batteries and hydrochloric acid, called spirits of salts, is a powerful cleaning agent.

Mineral acids would have a sour taste too if you tasted them. But they are strong acids and would burn your mouth. **Never taste anything in the laboratory**.

Properties of acids

Apart from having a sour taste, acids have other properties in common.

- They all turn blue litmus red.
- They all have a pH less than 7 (the lower the pH, the stronger the acid).
- They all contain hydrogen, which can be replaced by a metal to form a salt.
- They fizz when mixed with a carbonate, forming carbon dioxide gas.
- They all fizz when mixed with magnesium, forming hydrogen gas.
- They are corrosive and will burn your skin.

1 The table shows the properties of three liquids **A**, **B**, and **C**. Which one is an acid? Explain why you made this choice.

Liquid	Reaction with magnesium	Reaction with a carbonate	Blue litmus	Red litmus
A	does not fizz	does not fizz	stays blue	turns blue
B	fizzes	fizzes	turns red	stays red
C	does not fizz	does not fizz	stays blue	stays red

2 The chemical formulae of the three mineral acids are HNO_3, H_2SO_4, and HCl. Match each formula to its acid.

3 An acid has the formula H_3PO_4. Choose the name of this acid from the list below.

potassium acid   **phosphoric acid**   **phosphacid**

Finding out: Water in acids

In this experiment you are going to mix solid sodium hydrogencarbonate and solid citric acid. (Citric acid is the acid in lemons.) You will put the mixture into two dry test tubes. You will add water to one test tube and compare the reactions in the two tubes.

Instructions

1 Put three spatula measures of sodium hydrogencarbonate and three spatula measures of citric acid on a piece of paper. Mix the two chemicals thoroughly using the spatula.

2 Divide the mixture in half and put the halves into two dry test tubes.

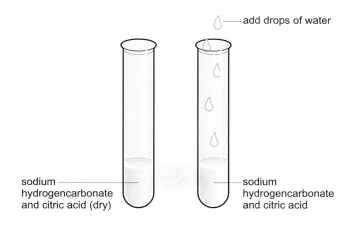

add drops of water

sodium hydrogencarbonate and citric acid (dry)

sodium hydrogencarbonate and citric acid

3 Add a small amount of water to one tube.

4 Add a small volume of water to one of the tubes, as shown in the diagram.

5 Record what you see in each test tube. Test any gas produced with limewater, as shown in the diagram below.

reacting mixture

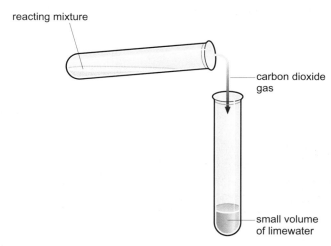

carbon dioxide gas

small volume of limewater

6 Pour the gas (but not the reacting mixture) into a test tube containing limewater. Shake the tube gently. If the limewater goes milky, the gas is carbon dioxide.

7 Copy and complete the table.

8 What does this experiment show?

Reaction mixture	Observations
sodium hydrogencarbonate and citric acid without water	
sodium hydrogencarbonate and citric acid with water	

Bases and alkalis

The jar contains oxygen. The iron is burning in the oxygen and forming iron oxide.

To make soaps, fats are heated with sodium hydroxide

Did You Know?

The word 'alkali' comes from an Arabic word *al-kali* which means burnt ashes. There is an alkali left in the ashes of a wood fire. The first soap was made by mixing the ashes from a fire with animal fat.

Forming a base

The photograph on the left shows a metal burning in oxygen to form a metal oxide. A metal oxide is called a **base**. A base is a substance that reacts with an acid.

Some bases dissolve in water. When a base dissolves in water, it forms an **alkali**. You might have used these common alkalis:

- sodium hydroxide, NaOH

- potassium hydroxide, KOH

- calcium hydroxide, $Ca(OH)_2$

- ammonium hydroxide (sometimes called ammonia solution), NH_4OH.

About alkalis

Dilute solutions of alkalis feel soapy. Alkalis are used for removing oil and grease (degreasing) and for making soap.

You need to take care when using alkalis. Like acids, they are corrosive, and are especially dangerous in the eyes.

1 Look at the names of the common alkalis. What do they all have in common?

2 How is ammonium hydroxide different from the other alkalis?

3 Ammonium hydroxide is made when ammonia gas is dissolved in water, H_2O. What is the chemical formula of ammonia?

4 Look at the Venn diagram below. At which point **A**, **B**, or **C** could the following be placed?

   a magnesium oxide   **b** sodium hydroxide   **c** water

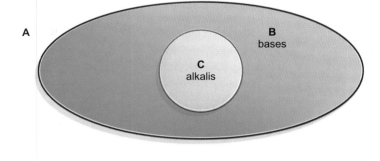

Neutralization

Acids have a pH lower than 7 and alkalis have a pH higher than 7. If an acid and an alkali are mixed in the correct volumes, a **neutral** solution is formed with a pH of 7. This process is called **neutralization**.

An acid contains hydrogen. In a neutralization reaction, this hydrogen is replaced by a metal. An alkali contains hydroxide. The hydrogen and hydroxide join together to form water during the neutralization reaction.

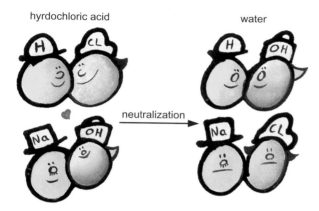

In a neutralization reaction, the hydrogen and hydroxide join to form water

An example of a neutralization reaction is the reaction between hydrochloric acid and sodium hydroxide shown in the picture above. The reaction produces a salt as well as water. In the picture the salt is sodium chloride. The salt produced depends on the acid and the alkali that you use.

- If you use hydrochloric acid you will get a **chloride**.
- If you use sulphuric acid you will get a **sulphate**.
- If you use nitric acid you will get a **nitrate**.

Did You Know?

When you brush against a stinging nettle, it injects an acid into your skin. Rubbing the sting with a dock leaf relieves the pain. A dock leaf contains a weak alkali. A neutralization reaction happens, which neutralizes the acid.

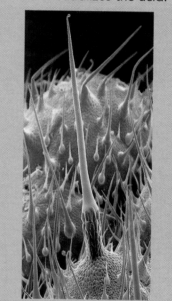

An injection from a stinging nettle can cause an allergic reaction

---

1 A solution containing sodium hydroxide and hydrochloric acid is evaporated to dryness. What is the white solid left?

2 Ten drops of hydrochloric acid are needed to neutralize 5 cm^3 of sodium hydroxide solution. What does this show about these solutions?

3 Copy these word equations and finish them using words from the list below.

carbonate   chloride   ethanoate   nitrate   sulphate

a potassium hydroxide + sulphuric acid → potassium _____ + water

b calcium hydroxide + nitric acid → calcium _____ + water

c lithium hydroxide + ethanoic acid → lithium _____ + water

d ammonium hydroxide + hydrochloric acid → ammonium _____ + water

e calcium hydroxide + carbonic acid → calcium _____ + water

Uses of neutralization

The farmer tests his soil to see how acidic it is

Treating indigestion

Have you ever had indigestion? Some people get indigestion after eating too much, or eating certain foods. Your stomach contains over 1000 cm^3 of hydrochloric acid. This does you no harm. It provides the right conditions in your stomach for digesting your food. During digestion, your food is broken down into simple chemicals which can be absorbed into your blood and used by your body. These chemicals are the vital supplies your body needs for all kinds of jobs including building new tissues, repairing damage, and providing energy by respiration.

Indigestion is caused by too much acid or **excess acidity**. You can cure indigestion by taking a medicine containing a weak alkali such as sodium hydrogencarbonate or magnesium hydroxide. The alkali will neutralize the excess acidity and relieve the pain.

Treating soil acidity

The photograph on the left shows a farmer testing the pH of the soil. Soil with a pH between 6.5 and 7.0 is best for growing a wide range of plants. If the pH falls below 6, the soil becomes too acidic for growing most crops. If the pH rises above 8, the soil becomes too alkaline.

There can be considerable differences in pH even in different fields on the same farm. It is important that the farmer knows the pH and controls it. Excess acidity in soil is the most important cause of crop failure. It causes 'soil sourness'. This happens because rainwater is slightly acidic. The excess acidity can be neutralized by adding lime (calcium hydroxide).

1 Indigestion medicines contain a weak alkali. Why would you not take a strong alkali to relieve indigestion?

2 Why is 'soil sourness' a good name for soil acidity?

3 Indigestion medicines are called antacids. Why are they called this? List any antacids you have heard of.

4 The photograph on the left shows a car battery spilling sulphuric acid onto a garage floor.

   a What could you do to clear up the spill?

   b Suppose a bulk tanker spilled acid onto a motorway after an accident. How would firefighters deal with it?

5 Antacid packets warn you to go to the doctor if the problem keeps coming back. Why do you think this is?

Salts

When you hear the word 'salt', you probably think of the white solid people put on their chips. This is sometimes called 'common salt' and the chemical name for it is sodium chloride. However, the word 'salt' refers to a large group of compounds. Sodium chloride is just one of many different salts.

What is a salt?

A **salt** is formed in a reaction in which one or more hydrogens in an acid is replaced by a metal (or ammonium). For example,

- sodium chloride, NaCl, is produced from hydrochloric acid, HCl
- potassium nitrate, KNO_3, is produced from nitric acid, HNO_3
- calcium sulphate, $CaSO_4$, is produced from sulphuric acid, H_2SO_4
- ammonium chloride, NH_4Cl, is produced from hydrochloric acid, HCl.

Properties of salts

Most salts are solids with high melting points. Some salts crystallize with a certain amount of water in their structure. This is called **water of crystallization**. For example, copper(II) sulphate crystals are sometimes called copper(II) sulphate-5-water or $CuSO_4.5H_2O$.

Most salts are soluble in water, but some are insoluble and some are only slightly soluble. It is important to know how easily the salt dissolves in water if you are planning how to make the salt.

Acid salts

Sulphuric acid, H_2SO_4, has two hydrogens that can be replaced. If both hydrogens are replaced you form a normal salt such as sodium sulphate, Na_2SO_4. If just one hydrogen is replaced you form an **acid salt** such as sodium hydrogensulphate, $NaHSO_4$.

If you heat copper(II) sulphate crystals hard, the water of crystallization is driven off. The white powder is anhydrous copper(II) sulphate (anhydrous means without water).

Did You Know?

Chemistry sets often contain crystals of sodium hydrogensulphate. It is sometimes called sodium bisulphate. Sulphuric acid is a liquid and would be difficult to pack safely without spilling. When sodium hydrogensulphate is dissolved in water, it behaves like dilute sulphuric acid.

1 Which acid would you use to make
   a a chloride   b a nitrate   c a sulphate?

2 Carbonic acid has the formula H_2CO_3. What salts are made from carbonic acid?

3 When barium chloride crystals are heated, a colourless liquid is formed.
   a How would you show this is water?
   b Where do you think it comes from?

4 Sodium hydrogencarbonate is an acid salt.
   a What is an acid salt?
   b What would happen if you tested sodium hydrogencarbonate solution with universal indicator?

Finding out: Solubility of salts

In this experiment you are going to test different salts to see if they are soluble in water. You will be given solutions of metal nitrates. All metal nitrates are soluble in water. You are going to convert each metal nitrate into three other salts to see if they are soluble.

- You are first going to add hydrochloric acid to the metal nitrate to make the metal chloride. For example, adding hydrochloric acid to calcium nitrate makes calcium chloride.

- Then you will add dilute sulphuric acid to the metal nitrate to produce the metal sulphate.

- Finally you will add sodium carbonate solution to make the metal carbonate.

If the salt produced is soluble in water, you will be able to see through the solution – it will be **transparent**. If the salt is insoluble, a cloudy solution will be formed. The salt has made a **precipitate**.

Instructions

1 Copy the following table.

2 Carry out each experiment. Write **soluble** if a transparent solution is formed and **insoluble** if a cloudy solution is formed.

3 Copy and complete the following sentences.

   a All metal nitrates are soluble in water.

b All metal chlorides are soluble in water except _____ chloride and _____ chloride.

c All metal sulphates are soluble in water except _____ sulphate and _____ sulphate.

d All metal carbonates are insoluble in water except _____ carbonate and _____ carbonate.

Metal nitrate solution	Add hydrochloric acid to form the metal chloride	Add sulphuric acid to form the metal sulphate	Add sodium carbonate to form the metal carbonate
sodium nitrate			
potassium nitrate			
barium nitrate			
calcium nitrate			
magnesium nitrate			
zinc nitrate			
iron(III) nitrate			
lead(II) nitrate			
copper(II) nitrate			
silver nitrate			

Preparing soluble salts

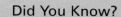

Magnesium sulphate is a soluble salt. It can be made by reacting sulphuric acid with, for example, magnesium oxide:

magnesium oxide + sulphuric acid → magnesium sulphate + water

The magnesium sulphate is dissolved in the reaction mixture. We need to remove the water from it. The process is shown in the photographs.

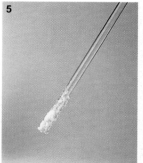

*Preparing magnesium sulphate: **1** Heat acid, adding magnesium oxide **2** Stir, add magnesium oxide until some remains **3** Filter **4** Gently heat the solution; the solution concentrates as water eveporates; dip a glass rod in from time to time **5** When the solution is ready crystals form on the rod when it cools in the air **6** As soon as the solution is ready, allow the basin to cool; crystals of magnesium sulphate will form*

Reacting and dissolving

People often confuse magnesium oxide *reacting* with dilute sulphuric acid with magnesium sulphate *dissolving* in water. After dissolving, you can recover the same substance when the water has evaporated but not after reacting.

---

1 Why is the sulphuric acid heated in stage **1** before the magnesium oxide is added?

2 In stage **2**, some magnesium oxide remains in the beaker after the mixture has been stirred for some time. Suggest why this happens.

3 In stage **3**, where does the unreacted magnesium oxide finish up?

4 What passes through the filter paper into the evaporating basin in stage **3**?

5 In stage **4**, the solution is heated until the point at which crystals would form on cooling. How is this point found?

6 Why is it important not to evaporate the solution to dryness in stage **4**?

7 Copy these word equations that show other ways of producing magnesium sulphate. Finish the equations.

a magnesium + sulphuric acid → magnesium sulphate + _____

b magnesium hydroxide + sulphuric acid → magnesium sulphate + _____

c magnesium carbonate + sulphuric acid → magnesium sulphate + _____ + _____

8 Copy and complete these sentences, using words from the list below.

new   reaction   same

When a substance reacts, a chemical _____ takes place and at least one _____ substance is formed. When a substance dissolves, the _____ substance is recovered on evaporation.

Finding out: Making copper(II) sulphate

In this experiment you are going to make copper(II) sulphate starting from black copper(II) oxide.

Instructions

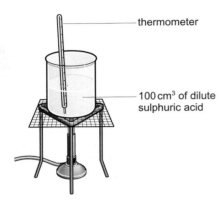

1 Put about 100 cm³ of dilute sulphuric acid into the beaker and heat to about 60 °C.

2 Add a spatula measure of copper(II) oxide to the acid and stir until the solid has disappeared.

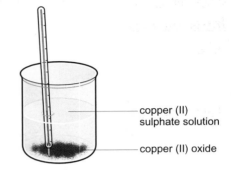

3 Put in more spatula measures of copper(II) oxide one by one, stirring after each one, until some copper(II) oxide remains.

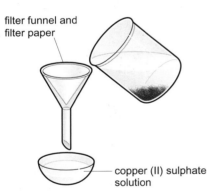

4 Filter the solution into an evaporating basin.

5 Evaporate the solution until only a small volume remains.

6 Leave the solution to cool. Crystals of copper(II) sulphate will form.

7 What colour is the solution formed when copper(II) oxide reacts with dilute sulphuric acid?

8 How is the unreacted copper(II) oxide removed from the solution?

9 Copy the word equation below and finish it.

copper(II) oxide + _____ _____ → _____ _____ + water

WARNING

Wear safety goggles

Finding out: Making sodium chloride

In this experiment you are going to make sodium chloride from sodium hydroxide and hydrochloric acid. You will do it twice. The first time you will use an indicator to find out how much acid you need to use. The second time you will do it without the indicator, so that your sodium chloride does not contain indicator. Sodium chloride is formed by evaporating the solution left at the end of the experiment.

> **WARNING**
>
> Wear safety goggles

Instructions

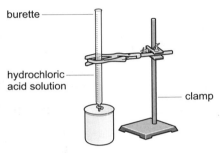

1 Fill the burette with hydrochloric acid, using a funnel. Remove the funnel and run acid out of the burette until the reading is zero.

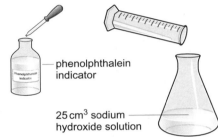

2 Use the measuring cylinder to put 25 cm³ of sodium hydroxide solution in the conical flask. Add three drops of phenolphthalein indicator.

3 Add acid from the burette in small portions, swirling the flask after each addition. Carry on until the solution just turns pink. Read the volume of acid added.

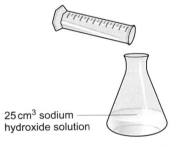

4 Wash out the flask and refill the burette. Measure out a new sample of 25 cm³ of sodium hydroxide solutions into the flask. **Do not** add phenolphthalein indicator.

5 Repeat stage **3**, adding the same volume of acid as before. (The solution will not go pink.)

6 Evaporate the solution until solid sodium chloride remains.

This type of experiment is called a **titration**.

7 Why did you not evaporate the solution in the first experiment?

8 Copy the word equation below and finish it.

sodium hydroxide + _____ _____ → _____ _____ + water

Preparing insoluble salts

An insoluble salt is prepared by a method called **precipitation**. For example, barium sulphate is insoluble in water. It can be prepared by mixing a solution containing a soluble barium compound with a solution containing a soluble sulphate.

The two solutions are mixed and a white precipitate is formed. This is barium sulphate. The white precipitate is removed by filtering. The precipitate will still contain some of the original solutions. It is therefore washed with distilled water and dried. The process is summarized in the photographs.

Purifying by precipitation

When water is purified, substances are added to the water to remove harmful dissolved substances. The harmful substances are precipitated. Heavy metals such as lead and cadmium can be removed by precipitation.

A mask prevents people breathing in poisonous lead compounds when sanding down old paintwork

Uses of insoluble salts

Insoluble salts are often used as pigments in paints. Pigments give paints their colour. Lead sulphate was used for many years in white paints, but it is poisonous. People need to be careful when removing old paint at home in case the paint contains lead. The dust can be poisonous.

1 Choose two solutions from the list below which could be mixed to prepare barium sulphate.

**barium carbonate   barium nitrate
sodium sulphate   lead sulphate**

2 Lead carbonate is an insoluble salt. Choose two solutions from the list below which could be mixed to prepare lead carbonate.

**lead sulphate   lead nitrate
calcium carbonate   sodium carbonate**

3 Sulphuric acid can be used to prepare barium sulphate from barium chloride solution. Write a word equation for the reaction.

4 Write down two solutions that you could mix to prepare lead sulphate.

5 Soluble barium compounds are poisonous. Barium sulphate is not poisonous. A pupil who has swallowed barium chloride is told to drink magnesium sulphate solution. Why?

Finding out: Making barium sulphate

In this experiment you are going to make the insoluble salt barium sulphate. You are going to mix two solutions, one containing a barium compound and the other containing a sulphate. The insoluble barium sulphate forms a precipitate. You can remove the precipitate from the solution by filtering, and then wash and dry it.

> **WARNING**
>
> Wear safety goggles
>
> Barium compounds are poisonous.

Instructions

barium nitrate solution

barium sulphate and solution

barium sulphate on filter paper

clear solution

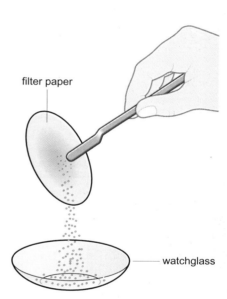

filter paper

watchglass

1 Pour barium nitrate solution into a beaker until it is about one-third full. Add about the same volume of sulphuric acid.

2 Stir the mixture and then pour it through a filter paper in a filter funnel. Pour water through the filter to wash the precipitate.

3 Scrape the solid into a watch glass and leave it to dry.

4 What colour was the precipitate that formed?

5 Write a word equation for the reaction that formed barium sulphate.

6 Now mix equal volumes of lead(II) nitrate solution and potassium iodide solution.

  a What colour is the precipitate formed?

  b What is the chemical name of the precipitate formed?

  c Write a word equation for the reaction.

CHAPTER 24

Charging by friction

Why do you sometimes get a shock after walking across a nylon carpet? What causes a rubbed balloon to stick to the ceiling? The answers to these questions are to do with **static electricity**, or electric charge that is not moving.

Rubbing a balloon

You can charge up a balloon by rubbing it with cotton cloth. Once it has been charged it will attract pieces of paper, stick to the wall or ceiling, and attract a stream of water flowing out of a tap.

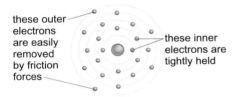

these outer electrons are easily removed by friction forces

these inner electrons are tightly held

electrons orbiting an atomic nucleus

Electrons rubbing off

The balloon is charged because electrons rub off the cloth onto it. Electrons are tiny negatively charged particles that form part of atoms. Some of these electrons are close to the nucleus of the atom. Others are at the outer edge of the atom and are easily removed, as shown in the diagram on the left.

Friction force

When two objects rub together, there is friction. This is the force that opposes slipping and sliding. The friction force between the cloth and the balloon pulls some electrons away from the atoms in the cloth onto the surface of the balloon.

The balloon gains electrons from the cloth. It now has more negative charges than positive charges so it has an overall negative charge. The cloth has lost electrons. It now has fewer negative charges than positive ones so it has an overall positive charge. Both the balloon and the cloth become charged when electrons move from one to the other.

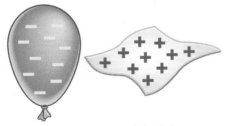

The balloon and the cloth both become charged when they are rubbed together

Did You Know?

Sailors on oil tankers wear special conducting shoes so that they do not become charged up by walking around and cause sparks to fly. The sparks could set off an explosion.

1 Write down three effects that are caused by electrostatic forces.

2 Draw diagrams to describe how a balloon and a cloth become charged when they are rubbed together.

3 Use diagrams to explain how you could show that

   a two objects with the same type of charge repel each other

   b two objects with opposite types of charge attract each other.

Attraction and repulsion

Using a van de Graaff generator can be a hair-raising experience!. Charged objects may be pulled towards each other or pushed away from each other, depending on the type of charge that each one has.

Pulling together

If you rub a balloon on your jumper, the jumper and the balloon stick together. The balloon gains electrons, giving it an overall negative charge. The jumper has an overall positive charge. Two objects with opposite charges are **attracted**. Each one pulls the other towards it. The forces between a charged balloon and the jumper are shown in the diagram below right.

Pushing away

If you rub two balloons on a cloth and hold them near to each other, they move away from each other. Two objects with the same type of charge are **repelled**. Each one pushes the other away. The forces between the two charged balloons are shown in the diagram bottom right.

Static charge

Charge cannot move through insulators such as plastic or rubber. When charge is placed on a balloon or a plastic rod, it stays put. This is known as **static charge**.

Charge can move through good conductors such as a metal. It can also move through poor conductors such as human beings. When you walk across a nylon carpet, the friction forces between your feet and the carpet cause charge to build up on both you and the carpet.

The moment you touch a conductor in contact with the Earth, you become discharged. A flow of charge passes between you and the Earth. This is what happens if you touch the earthed screw on a light switch. The movement of charge between your body and the earth gives you an electric shock.

Van de Graaff generator: the like charges push the hairs away from each other

The balloon and the jumper attract each other

Two charged balloons push away from each other

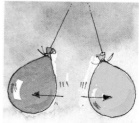

---

1 How could you find out whether two charged objects have the same type of charge or opposite types of charge?

2 Imagine that you are wearing a woollen skirt or trousers and sitting on a chair that has a plastic frame and metal legs.

   a Describe how you and the chair become charged as you shuffle on it.

b Explain why you receive a shock when you touch the metal legs.

3 Water molecules are polarized. They behave as if one end has a negative charge and the other end has a positive charge. Explain why water is attracted to both negatively charged objects and positively charged objects.

Moving charge around

Why does a charged balloon stick to the uncharged ceiling and attract uncharged pieces of paper? Why is hair attracted to objects of either charge? The reason is a process called **electrostatic induction**.

Using hair conditioner

You can tell when your hair needs washing. It feels greasy as it becomes coated with natural oils. Shampoo removes the oils, leaving the hair dry. Dry hair is a good insulator and it easily becomes charged when you put a jumper on over your head. This makes the hair stick up, as all the hairs have the same type of charge and repel each other. To avoid this, most shampoos either have a built-in hair conditioner or the label recommends that you use a separate hair conditioner.

Hair conditioners contain both positively and negatively charged ions that allow charge to move along the surface of hair. If the hair becomes charged by rubbing, it is quickly discharged by the movement of these ions.

Why does hair become attracted to a charged object of either type? This is because of the movement of ions along the hair. The diagram shows what happens when a negatively charged balloon is held near the hair. The hair becomes temporarily charged in a process known as **induction**. When the balloon is removed, the charges on the hair move back.

Painting with charge

Electrostatic induction happens because charges move around. It can be used to do useful jobs in agriculture and manufacturing. Electrostatic induction is used to spray crops and metal panels more efficiently.

The diagram shows a metal panel being sprayed with paint in the form of a powder. The panel is connected electrically to earth. This allows electrons to move between the panel and the earth.

As the powder leaves the nozzle, it is given a positive charge. The metal panel becomes charged by induction, as the positively charged paint particles attract electrons from the earth. This in turn causes the paint to be attracted to the panel, as they now have opposite charges. This means the panel is evenly painted and less paint is wasted.

Hair conditioner stops your hair from standing on end

The balloon attracts positive ions and repels negative ones

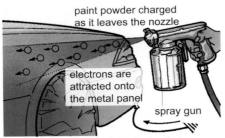

paint powder charged as it leaves the nozzle

electrons are attracted onto the metal panel

spray gun

Painting by electrostatic induction

Did You Know?

Electrostatic forces were known to the ancient Greeks. They knew that rubbing a fossilized resin that we call amber made it attract dust. The Greek name for amber is elektron, which is how the electron got its name.

 1 Draw a diagram to explain how hair is attracted to a positively charged object.

2 Explain why the induction process cannot be used to spray plastic objects.

3 Explain how the induction process would work if a metal panel was sprayed with negatively charged particles.

Charge and current

Electric charge can sometimes cause dramatic effects such as sparks and lightning. What happens when a spark passes from a van de Graaff generator? What happens when lightning strikes?

Using charge to light a lamp

When current from the mains passes through a fluorescent lamp it gives out light. The photograph shows how a van de Graaff generator gives out light when a charge passes through it. The second photograph shows how it also gives out light when the charge from a van de Graaff generator passes through it. This gives a clue about the relationship between charge and current – current is simply charge on the move.

Van de Graaff generator

A lightning strike

When lightning strikes, charge from a cloud passes through the air into the ground. Normally air is an insulator. To make it into a conductor it has to be ionized. There is a high voltage between the base of a thundercloud and earth. This causes electrons to be pulled off air particles, creating both positive and negative ions. The positive ions move towards the cloud and the negative ions move towards the ground. This movement of ions is an electric current.

The movement of ions in a lightning strike

Current in a metal

Unlike air, a metal does not have to be ionized before charge can pass through it. Metals are made up of fixed positive ions along with negative electrons that are free to move. When a voltage is applied to a metal, the free electrons drift from the negative terminal towards the positive terminal. The movement is quite slow, about a few millimetres each second, as the electrons undergo frequent collisions.

negative Cl^- ions   positive Na^+ ions
move to the positive   move to the negative
electrode   electrode

Electrolysis: the movement of ions in molten sodium chloride

Current in gases and conducting liquids

The current in a metal is carried by moving free electrons. In a conducting gas or liquid, both positive and negative ions move in opposite directions to carry the current. Gases give out light when they conduct electricity. Different gases give out light of different colours. This makes them useful in illuminated signs.

1. Explain how the current in a metallic conductor is different from the current in an ionized gas.

2. Explain why a gas needs to be ionized before it can conduct electricity.

3. Some illuminated signs give out light when an electric current passes through the gas neon. Use a diagram to explain how neon conducts electricity.

Did You Know?

You should never shelter under a tree in a lightning storm. The safest place to be is inside a metal object such as a car or train. If you are out in the open, lying flat on the ground is the best way of avoiding a lightning strike.

The field of a current

What makes a magnet magnetic? What causes the Earth's magnetic field? How do electromagnets work? To help you find out about magnetism you can study magnetic fields that are caused by *electric currents*.

The simple field

Every electric current has its own **magnetic field**. This is a region where the current exerts forces on magnetic materials such as iron and steel. Switch the current off and the magnetic field disappears. Switch the current on and the magnetic field is there again. However, when you turn on a light you do not see every magnetic object in the room being attracted to the wires carrying the current. In most cases the magnetic field is very weak.

You can investigate the magnetic field around a wire carrying a current using iron filings and plotting compasses. The diagram on the right shows the field pattern due to a current passing in a wire. It consists of concentric circles (circles with the same centre) around the wire. The direction of the field is clockwise when viewed in the direction of the current. This means that the N-seeking pole of a magnet has a force on it in the clockwise direction.

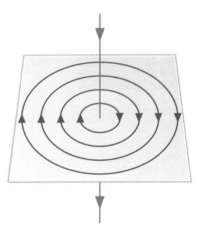

The magnetic field due to a current passing in a wire

The coil and the solenoid

One way of making a stronger magnetic field is to wind the wire into a coil. A long, tightly wound coil is called a **solenoid**. The diagrams below show the magnetic field patterns due to currents passing in a coil and in a solenoid.

You can magnetize a piece of iron or steel by placing it inside a solenoid with the current switched on and leaving it there for some time.

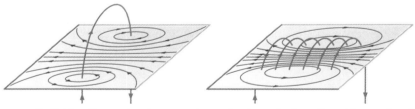

The magnetic field patterns due to current passing in a single coil and in a solenoid

1 Describe how you would use iron filings and a plotting compass to find the shape and direction of the magnetic field around a single current-carrying wire.

2 Eight small compasses are arranged in a circle around a wire. The current is switched off.

  a Explain why the compasses all point in the same direction.

  b Describe and explain what you expect to happen when a current passes in the wire.

  c What would happen if you reversed the current in the wire?

3 a In what way is the magnetic field of a solenoid similar to that of a bar magnet?

  b Explain how the direction of the magnetic field inside a solenoid is different from the direction outside the solenoid.

Every electric current has its own magnetic field, but these magnetic fields are often very weak. You need to make careful observations in this practical work.

Instructions

1 Arrange a length of wire so that it passes vertically through a hole in the centre of a horizontal card.

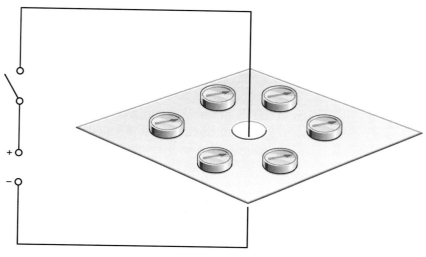

2 Place a few small compasses in a circle around the wire. Which way should they point? Check to make sure.

3 Connect the wire to a power supply so that the direction of the current passing in the wire is down (positive to negative).

4 Note what happens to the compass needles when the current is switched on. They point in the direction of the magnetic field caused by the current. Check by turning the current off and on several times.

5 Make sketches of what you see when the current is turned off and when the current is turned on.

6 What do you think will happen if the current is reversed? Try it and see.

7 Remove the compasses. With the current switched on, gently sprinkle iron filings onto the card around the wire. Tap the card so that the iron filings align themselves with the magnetic field.

8 Sketch the pattern of the magnetic field and describe it in words. Compare your sketch with the one on the next page.

Electromagnets

Electromagnets are used to make motors turn and to record information on computer disks and tapes. Some trains do not have motors or engines, but are powered directly by electromagnets built into the track.

For an electromagnet to do a useful job, the magnetic field needs to be made stronger.

Using a core

A useful electromagnet can be made by coiling a length of wire into a solenoid. The magnetic field is still weak. It will not pick up a paper clip and hardly affects iron filings. You can make an electromagnet stronger if you put a material in the middle of the solenoid, called the **core**.

Using iron in the core of an electromagnet makes it 2000 times as strong as the same electromagnet with an air core. An electromagnet with an iron core can exert forces big enough to move magnetic objects. It can pick up paper clips, as shown in the diagram. When the current in the coil is switched on, the magnetic field of the solenoid magnetizes the iron, which has a much stronger magnetic field than the solenoid on its own.

Another useful property of iron is that it is easy to magnetize. This means that when the current in an iron-cored electromagnet is switched on, the strong magnetic field is set up very quickly. When the current in an iron-cored electromagnet is switched off, it quickly loses most of its magnetism, but it keeps some.

What else makes an electromagnet stronger?

Apart from the material in the core, there are a number of other things that could affect the strength of an electromagnet:

- the number of turns of wire on the coil
- the length of the coil and core
- the size of the current passing in the coil.

These would be good topics for a science investigation.

This train is powered by electromagnets built into the track

Did You Know?

In an electron microscope, electromagnets are used to focus beams of electrons. This is similar to using lenses to focus light in an optical microscope.

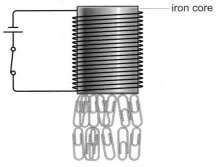

iron core

This iron-cored electromagnet can pick up a lot of paper clips ...

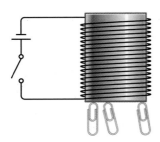

... and it hangs on to some of them when the current is switched off

---

1 Explain how using an iron core makes an electromagnet stronger.

2 How could you compare two electromagnets to find out which is stronger? Use a diagram and state clearly how you would tell which magnet is stronger.

3 Iron is easy to magnetize and it loses its magnetism readily. Steel is hard to magnetize and it keeps its magnetism. Explain why these properties make iron useful for the core of an electromagnet and steel useful for making permanent magnets.

Using electromagnets

Electromagnets are used in many domestic and industrial devices. They are used for lifting, sorting, and moving objects as well as for recording information.

Moving things around

Iron-cored electromagnets can exert large forces, and this makes them useful for moving heavy objects made out of iron or steel.

The crane shown in the photograph uses cylindrical electromagnets. The coil is wound between the inner and outer rings of the iron core, as shown in the diagram below. When current passes in the coil, these rings behave like the opposite poles of a magnet. The object being lifted is attracted to both magnetic poles.

This electromagnet is moving scrap metal in a scrapyard

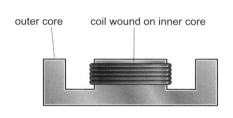
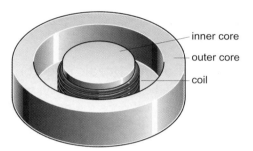

outer core coil wound on inner core

inner core
outer core
coil

Did You Know?

The picture that you see on a television or computer monitor is made up of dots of three colours. The dots appear where beams of electrons strike the screen. The beams of electrons are moved very rapidly by electromagnets.

Recording music and video

Cassette tapes are used to record music and video. These store the information about sounds and pictures in magnetized regions on the tape. The tape has a thin layer of magnetic material on it. This layer can be magnetized by placing it in a magnetic field. A **recording head** is an electromagnet with a small gap in the core. The coil of the electromagnet carries a high frequency alternating current – this means it changes direction several thousand times each second. As the tape passes over the gap, it becomes magnetized. The magnetic pattern recorded on the tape contains all the information about the sound or picture. It can be decoded by playing the tape back over a similar device, called a **playback head**.

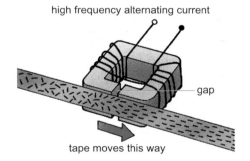

high frequency alternating current

gap

tape moves this way

A recording head records information by magnetizing the tape

---

1 In a foundry, metals are melted down to be reused. Draw a diagram to explain how an electromagnet can sort the iron and steel from other metals.

2 The diagram shows the poles of a cylindrical magnet. Copy the diagram and sketch on it the magnetic field that you would expect to find between the poles.

3 The magnetic tape used in audio and video recorders consists of a thin layer of magnetic material on a plastic tape.

   a Suggest why the tape used in video recording is wider than the tape used for audio recording.

   b How important is it that the tape is made from a material that does not stretch? Explain your answer fully.

The electric bell

Bells can signal good news (the start of a lesson) or bad news (the end of a lesson or a fire drill). They work because of electromagnetism. A very clever circuit repeatedly turns the electromagnet on and off.

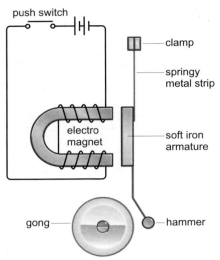

This bell circuit only 'dings' once

The electromagnet and the armature

It is easy to make a bell that goes 'ding'. All you need is a circuit with an electromagnet and a moving part called an **armature**. The armature is made of a magnetic material. When the electromagnet is switched on, it attracts the armature. The hammer attached to the armature strikes the gong. The diagram on the left shows the circuit.

This bell has one major drawback – it only 'dings' once. To release the armature from the electromagnet, the push switch has to be opened. So the only way to make a continuous ring is to keep pushing and then releasing the switch.

The make and break circuit

To make the bell ring repeatedly, you need a mechanism that switches the electromagnet off once the gong has been struck. The springy metal strip pulls the armature away from the elctromagnet. The electromagnet then needs to be switched back on again. This repeated switching on and off is carried out using a circuit called a **make-and-break circuit**. A make-and-break circuit causes itself to be switched on and off repeatedly. The complete circuit is shown in the diagram on the left.

This is what happens when the push switch is closed.

- The coil of the electromagnet magnetizes the core.
- The magnetized core attracted the armature, so the hammer strikes the gong.
- The circuit is broken at the contact screw, switching the electromagnet off.
- The armature springs back.
- The circuit is made at the contact screw, switching the electromagnet on.

This process is repeated until the circuit is broken at the push switch.

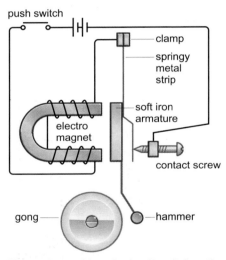

The make-and-break circuit switches the electromagnet on and off repeatedly. The bells rings continuously.

Did You Know?

The sparks that ignite the petrol and air mixture in an engine are produced by a make-and-break circuit. When the current in an electromagnet is switched off, a large voltage is produced which causes a spark between two electrodes.

1 In a bell, the armature is made of iron. Explain why iron is used rather than steel.

2 Explain why the armature needs to be attached to a springy metal strip.

3 You can adjust the frequency with which the hammer strikes the gong by moving the contact screw towards or away from the armature. Explain how each of these movements affects the frequency.

Relaying information

A **relay** is a hidden switch. If you want to turn the television on from your armchair, all you need to do is send a signal in the form of an infra-red beam. A relay inside the television set then switches it on. Relays are used to switch headlights in cars and to operate burglar alarms.

What is a relay and how does it work?

A relay is a switch like an ordinary light switch. It works by pressing two contacts together to complete a circuit. Instead of using a person's finger to press the switch contacts together, it uses an electromagnet.

The diagram on the right shows a relay. This is what happens when the current in the coil is switched on.

- The magnetic field of the coil magnetizes the iron core.
- The top of the L-shaped armature is pulled to the iron core.
- The armature rotates, pressing the switch contacts together.

When the current is switched off, the armature springs back and the switch contacts separate.

Why are relays so useful?

Only a small current is needed to operate the electromagnet, but the switch contacts can switch much larger currents. Relays are used in cars, where large currents are needed to operate devices such as the lights, starter motor, and rear screen heater. Thick wires are needed to carry these currents. Using a relay to do the switching means that thin wires can be used for the driver's switches, because they only need to switch small currents. The diagram on the right shows how a relay is used to switch on the large current to the motor that starts a car engine.

Relays are also used in low voltage control circuits which operate mains devices. In an immersion heater an electronic timing circuit uses a low voltage direct current. To turn on the immersion heater, a low voltage direct current passes in a relay coil. The relay switch contacts turn on the mains voltage supply to the immersion heater.

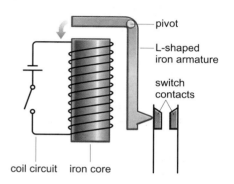

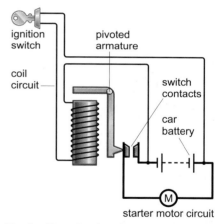

The ignition circuit only carries a small current, but the starter motor circuit carries a much larger current

1 What are the advantages of using a relay as a switch?

2 Draw a circuit diagram to show how a relay can be used so that a low voltage direct current can switch on a high voltage alternating current.

3 Write down two advantages of using a relay in a circuit to switch car headlights on and off.

Finding out: How a relay works

In this practical you will build your own relay. Your relay will use a single cell to switch a 12 V lamp operated from a power pack.

Instructions

1 First make the relay coil by winding a 1.5 m length of insulated wire around a C-core. All the windings should be in the same direction. Remember to leave 10–15 cm of wire at each end to connect to the cell.

2 Check that the relay coil is working. When you connect the cell to the coil, it should attract an iron object (use a hacksaw blade to test it). When you disconnect the cell, it should release the hacksaw blade.

3 Clamp a hacksaw blade horizontally so that it rests about 0.5 cm above the C-core, as shown in the diagram on the right. Check that the hacksaw blade is attracted to the C-core and touches it when the cell is connected, and springs away when the cell is disconnected.

4 Wire the lamp to the power supply. Make a switch using wires taped to the C-core and a wooden block. The diagram on the right shows how to do this.

5 When you connect the cell, the hacksaw blade should be attracted to the C-core. This should then switch on the lamp. Check that your relay works when you connect and disconnect the cell.

6 Write a description of how your relay operates.

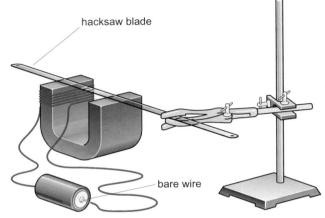

Making the electromagnet

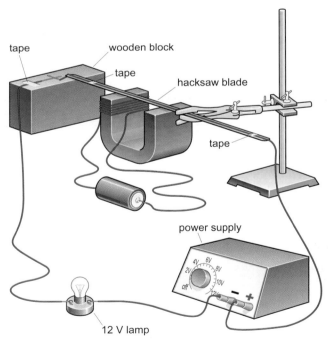

The complete relay and lamp circuit

Making a motor

A simple d.c. motor is made from an electromagnet and fixed magnets. You may have a kit at school for making a motor, but if you are prepared to improvise you can make a motor at home.

Using a kit

Follow these instructions to make a motor with a kit.

1 Wind about 1 m of wire onto the armature, taking particular care with the connections.
2 Prepare the baseboard. The wires to the low voltage supply should have bare ends. They should cross over at the point where they will connect with the armature.
3 Make sure that the slab magnets have opposite poles facing.
4 Slide the armature into place so that the low voltage wires separate but are pressed against the connections to the coil.
5 Switch on the power supply. You may need to give the motor a push to start it spinning.

A home-made motor

You can make a working motor without using a special kit. You can make the armature by winding a coil around the cork from a wine bottle. A round pencil pushed through the centre of the cork acts as an axle.

You can make connections to the coil using paper clips held in place by drawing pins. The pins can be pushed into a piece of wood for a baseboard.

A motor needs a large current. Rechargeable or alkaline batteries are best for this.

The diagram below shows a simple home-made motor.

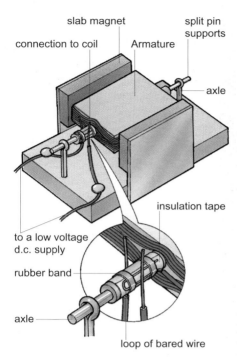

Making a motor from a kit

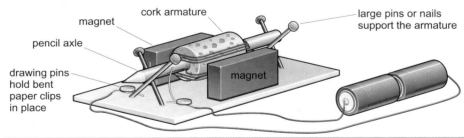

 1 The magnets in a motor need to have opposite poles facing. How can you tell when the opposite poles of two magnets are facing each other?

2 Explain why the metal axle of the kit motor needs to be covered with insulating tape before the coil is wound on the armature.

3 How could you measure the greatest weight that a motor can lift? Draw a diagram to show the arrangement that you would use.

Did You Know?

An electric motor works because a current-carrying wire moves in a magnetic field. This was first noticed by the French physicist André Ampère in 1820. The unit of current, the amp, is named after Ampère.

Getting BIGGER

A question of size

Have you ever looked at living things and wondered why they are the size and shape that they are? Why is a fish flattened on both sides? Why are leaves usually flat? Why is a cactus rounded with spines? How did huge dinosaurs manage to walk, let alone run? Why is an albatross's wing different from a kestrel's?

Why are leaves flat? You will find out later in this topic.

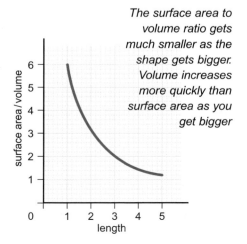

Activity

1 Make a cube out of plasticine that is 2 cm × 2 cm × 2 cm. What is the surface area?

2 Now change it so that it measures 4 cm × 2 cm × 1 cm. The volume stays the same, as you have not added or removed plasticine. What is the surface area?

3 Now make some other regular shapes from the same amount of plasticine. Record the dimensions and the surface area.

4 What pattern is there to your results?

5 What shape of plasticine would have the smallest surface area?

Surface area and volume

To begin to understand why organisms have the shapes they do, let's start with something simple. What happens if you make a shape bigger? Suppose you have an animal shaped like a cube. What will happen to the surface area and the volume if we double the length of the side?

- It has a length of 1 cm.
- Each side has a surface area of $1 \text{ cm} \times 1 \text{ cm} = 1 \text{ cm}^2$. So the whole cube, having six sides, has a surface area of 6 cm².
- The cube has a volume of $1 \text{ cm} \times 1 \text{ cm} \times 1 \text{ cm} = 1 \text{ cm}^3$.
- Now the length is 2 cm.
- The area of one side is $2 \text{ cm} \times 2 \text{ cm} = 4 \text{ cm}^2$. The total surface area is $6 \times 4 \text{ cm}^2 = 24 \text{ cm}^2$.
- The volume is $2 \text{ cm} \times 2 \text{ cm} \times 2 \text{ cm} = 8 \text{ cm}^3$.

So if we double the length, the surface area gets 4 times bigger and the volume gets 8 times bigger.

To compare the surface area and the volume of an object, we divide the surface area by the volume. This is called the **surface area to volume ratio**. If the figure is small, the shape has a large surface area compared with its volume. If the figure is large, the shape has a small surface area compared with its volume.

The surface area to volume ratio gets much smaller as the shape gets bigger. Volume increases more quickly than surface area as you get bigger

surface area / volume (y-axis, values 1–6)
length (x-axis, values 0–5)

Is size a problem?

You have seen that if a shape gets bigger, its surface area and volume change differently. All living things grow and so get bigger during their lives. Even a single cell can get larger. How do the changing surface area and volume affect an organism as it gets bigger?

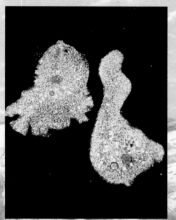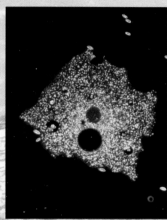

Even a single cell like an Amoeba grows until it reaches full size

Animals usually change shape as they grow

Volume matters

Some living processes depend on volume. For example, you need more food if you are bigger. This is because you need more material for building and repair, and you need more energy to stay alive. Because of this you also need more water and oxygen as well. Being bigger also makes you heavier, so you need more support. All of these needs depend on the amount of living tissue – in other words, on your volume.

Surface area matters

Other processes depend on the amount of surface area you have. Food, oxygen, and water all have to enter the body through a surface. Wastes like urea and carbon dioxide have to be removed across a surface. Heat is lost through the body surface. All of these processes depend on surface area. Odd though it may seem, the strength of your muscles is also related to their surface area and not their volume.

Big problems

There can be a problem with getting bigger. The amount of materials and energy you need go up very quickly, as does the volume. The means of getting these materials goes up more slowly, like the surface area. Eventually you reach a point where you need more energy than you can obtain.

---

1 The table below shows processes that depend on volume and processes that depend on area. Copy the table and complete it, matching up the following processes. Two have been done for you.

using food   heat loss   respiration rate
using oxygen to release energy   absorbing food
absorbing oxygen   needing water   muscle
strength   giving out carbon dioxide   giving out
wastes   increased weight   heat production

Processes depending on volume	Processes depending on area
using food	absorbing food
using oxygen to release energy	absorbing oxygen

2 Why do you need more oxygen if you need more energy?

3 Explain the problem of getting bigger.

4 Why might animals need to change shape as they get bigger?

Solving the surface area problem

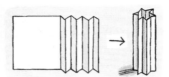

Another advantage of a shape with a large surface area is for support when flying

The main problem with getting bigger is that you do not have enough surface area to absorb the materials you need. How do living things solve this problem?

Activity

1 Find a single large potato (about 500 g in mass).

2 Find several small potatoes that together have the same mass as the large one.

3 Very carefully peel each potato separately. Make sure the peel is as thin and even as possible. Try not to take extra bits of potato without skin on them.

4 Lay each set of peelings out on squared paper. Estimate the area the peel covers in both cases.

5 Which has the larger surface area, the small potatoes or the large one?

6 Do both lots of potatoes have the same volume? How do you know?

7 Think about a large organ like the liver. How could you increase its surface area without increasing its size very much?

Activity

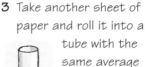
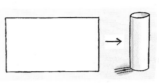
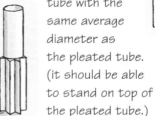
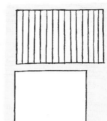
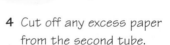

1 Take a sheet of paper and pleat it as shown in the diagram.

2 Join the two ends and make it into a tube.

3 Take another sheet of paper and roll it into a tube with the same average diameter as the pleated tube. (it should be able to stand on top of the pleated tube.)

4 Cut off any excess paper from the second tube.

5 Flatten out both sheets of paper and compare their surface areas.

6 What is the difference in area between the two sheets?

7 How could you increase the surface area inside a tube without making it any wider?

8 a What is the lining of the gut like?

   b Explain why it has this shape.

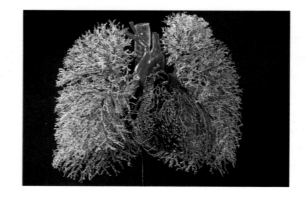

Your lungs are folded inside you. The surface of the lungs is so big it would cover a tennis court if it was spread out. This large surface helps you absorb the oxygen you need from the air, and get rid of carbon dioxide

Absorbing matters

Living things have many ways of solving the surface area problem. They all depend on either folding the surface layer, or flattening it.

Taking in oxygen

One of the most important things all animals need is oxygen. Fish and prawns have gills with many thin filaments. These fold outwards. They increase the surface area and help the fish absorb oxygen from the water. Vertebrates that live on land have lungs. These have lots of folds inwards. The folds (alveoli) give a large surface area for taking in oxygen. Insects have a system of tubes called tracheae which fold in to give a large surface area for taking in oxygen.

Tadpoles have gills that fold outwards. This gives them more surface area to take in oxygen.

Taking in food and water

We also need to take in food and water. Most animals have a gut with a folded lining. The most folded area is where the digested food molecules are absorbed. Plants have root hairs which stick out into the soil to collect water and minerals. The fine hairs create a huge surface area.

Flat as a pancake

Animals like the tapeworm are flat so they have a large surface area. A tapeworm lives inside a person's gut, where there is little oxygen. Its flat shape gives it a large surface for taking in food, water, and oxygen. Leaves are also flat to give a large surface area. This helps them absorb more sunlight, and take in carbon dioxide from the air.

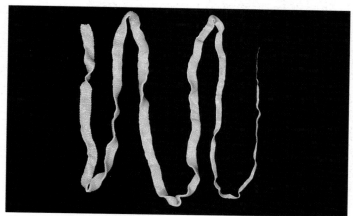

The flat surface of this tapeworm gives a large area on both sides

Folding inside cells

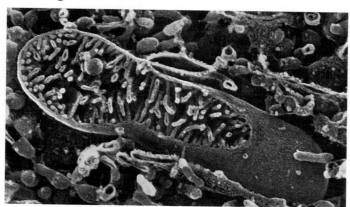

This photograph shows the folded membranes inside a mitochondrion

Even inside cells, structures are folded to increase their surface area. Mitochondria have folded layers to increase the surface area for respiration. Chloroplasts are made up of folded membranes. This means they can hold more chlorophyll for photosynthesis.

1 What are the two main ways of increasing surface area?

2 What gives mitochondria and chloroplasts a large internal surface area?

3 Why would plants living in the shade need bigger leaves than those in bright sunshine?

Surface issues

So far we have looked at how organisms make their surface area bigger. But a large surface area can cause problems of its own. Heat is lost from the surface. Water is also lost from the surface to the air.

Heat loss

Heat loss can be very important for animals that normally keep their body temperature constant. Chemical reactions in your body slow down if you get colder, and below a certain temperature they will not be fast enough to keep you alive. On the other hand, some animals need to lose heat if they live in a hot place.

Water loss

Living things depend on water. Water evaporates from the surface of organisms that live on land. Your lungs are folded inside your body, which helps prevent water loss. Some plants have leaves rolled into tubes for the same reason.

Elephant ears have a large surface area. They help the elephant lose heat so it doesn't overheat in the hot sun

Marram grass grows on beaches where the salt water tends to dry it out. Its leaves roll into a long tube to reduce the evaporation of water

Activity

1 Take two flasks of different sizes but the same shape.

2 Fill both with boiling water and put a thermometer in each.

3 Every minute, measure the temperature in each flask.

4 Plot your results for each flask as a line graph, using the same axes for both.

5 Which flask lost heat faster?

6 Which flask had the bigger surface area?

7 Calculate the surface area to volume ratio for each flask. Which one has most surface area for each unit of volume?

8 Why might a mouse have more problems surviving in the Arctic than a bear?

Activity

1 Take a sheet of blotting paper. Working on a tray, cut it into 4 equal pieces.

2 Leave one quarter as it is.

3 Cut one of the others into 3 pieces and lay them on top of each other.

4 Cut the next quarter into 4 and pile up the pieces.

5 Cut the last quarter into 8 and make another pile.

6 Pour 100 cm^3 of water onto each pile.

7 Time how long it takes for each pile to dry out. (You might speed this up by using a hair dryer, but you must make sure that each pile is dried equally.

8 Which pile of paper took longest to dry?

9 Which pile has the smallest surface area?

10 Plants living in dry conditions usually have small leaves and a round body shape. Why do you think this is?

11 Why do animals living in the desert usually come out at night and sleep during the day?

12 Why do many plants shed their leaves in winter?

Life in WATER

We have looked at the problems of getting bigger. You have seen how surface area limits the size of an organism. Now you are going to look at the different shapes of organisms living in different conditions.

Moving through water

We believe life started in the sea. Many life forms still live in the water, either in the sea or in fresh water. What problems do they face? The first problem is that water is much denser than air. This means that when you move through it there is a lot of friction. To reduce this friction, animals that move through water have evolved a **streamlined** shape. This is a smooth shape that helps the animal move through the water without causing turbulence. Streamlined shapes in nature have been copied by humans in ship building.

There are many streamlined shapes but they all have the same principle. The front end is wider than the back. This reduces turbulence as the organism moves and so reduces the drag effect of the water on the body. Many animals have become flattened which also helps them move smoothly through the water.

This fish has a streamlined shape to reduce friction as it swims

This squid is streamlined for swimming backwards!

Up and down

Being denser than air, water is better at supporting your weight. However, the pressure in deep water is much greater than the pressure in shallow water. Moving up and down in water creates problems of pressure and balance. Some animals keep their balance because of their shape. Some sharks have tails with a top lobe bigger than the bottom one. This tends to push them downwards. The body is flattened from top to bottom. This tends to push them upwards. Overall the shark is able to stay level in the water. Many animals have fins that help them stay upright, or help them steer.

The shark's body shape helps it stay balanced in the water

Branching and spreading

Plants and animals that do not move around may have branching shapes which are easily supported by the water. This means they can be very large and spreading without problems of support.

Water supports these organisms so they can spread out without breaking up

1 Why is a streamlined shape important in water?

2 What sort of shape is a streamlined shape?

3 Why are plants able to spread out easily in water?

4 Why might you expect to find bigger animals in the sea than on land?

Life in the AIR

The pteranodon was one of the largest flying dinosaurs

Light as a feather

Have you ever picked up a live chicken, or other medium-sized bird? They are surprisingly light. They have to be light to be able to get off the ground. Muscles can only generate enough power to lift about 25 kg into the air. Heavier than that and you become flightless (or need an engine to fly!).

Insects were the first group of animals to evolve powered flight

Birds were not the first flying animals on the Earth. The insects were here before them, then the dinosaurs, then birds, and finally some mammals evolved flight (bats).

The air gives some support, but it has a very low density. Large surfaces are needed to support a flying animal. Insects evolved wings from their outer skeletons. Birds evolved feathers from scales, and their front limbs became modified into wings. Bats and dinosaurs called pteranodons had skin stretched between the front and back legs. These are all different ways of having a large surface area but staying light.

Streamlining

Flying animals have problems of turbulence. Currents in the air can easily drag them off course. They need to use lots of energy to fly in the right direction. So flying organisms are streamlined in a similar way to fish. Humans have copied shapes from animals when they designed aeroplanes.

Birds have different shaped wings depending on the way they fly. Long thin wings are very useful for gliding, as in the albatross. Short wings are fine for short flights between perches, as in the sparrow. Hawks have wing shapes and movement which help them hover over their prey.

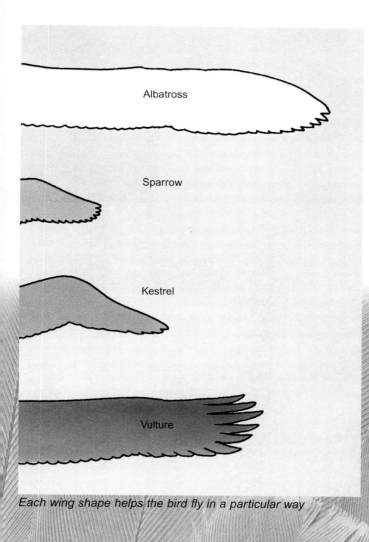

Albatross

Sparrow

Kestrel

Vulture

Each wing shape helps the bird fly in a particular way

?

1 What is the main problem facing flying animals?

2 Why do flying animals need to be streamlined?

3 Look at the outline of the vulture's wing. How do you think the shape helps the vulture spend a lot of time in the air?

4 Condors, the heaviest birds of prey, often rest in a tree after a meal. Why do they not fly off at once?

Other flying organisms

Many living things have found ways of moving through the air without using energy to fly through it. Many plants use the wind to spread their pollen or seeds. Spiders use their silk as a parachute to carry them long distances on air currents.

Dandelions are very successful at spreading their seeds

97

Life on LAND

When life first evolved onto land, it faced new problems, mainly getting enough water, and not drying out. Air also gives less support than water and so you weigh much more on land. Land organisms changed shape to help cope with these two difficulties.

Roots and shoots

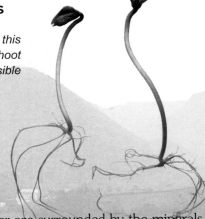

Even early in the life of this plant, the root and shoot structures are clearly visible

Algae that live in water are surrounded by the minerals and water they need. They only have to make sure they can get to the light. They have a fairly uniform structure. Plants on land have the minerals and water they need below them, while the light they need comes from above them. To cope with this, plants have a definite root and shoot structure. They have a transport system to connect these two structures going down and up. This allowed land plants to get really big.

Limbs

Animals on land have limbs that support their weight, but also allow them to move quickly. Many large animals such as birds and dinosaurs moved on two legs instead of four. Animals that live on land are often more compact than those living in water because of the weight problem. A giant squid could not live on land even if it could breathe air, as its body would collapse.

Newts live both in water and on land. Their legs are splayed out sideways from their bodies. Most mammals have legs under their bodies. This allows them to move on land more easily

Conserving water

To help prevent water loss, land animals developed lungs and special skins. The hard-shelled eggs of birds and insects help stop the developing young from drying out. Plants that live in very dry conditions have special features to conserve water. Cacti that live in the desert have spines instead of leaves, have a spherical shape to reduce their surface area, and store water in their stems.

The spines and spherical shape of a cactus help reduce water loss

1 What are the two main problems faced by life on land?

2 How have plants evolved to cope with these problems?

3 Why would having legs under the body be an advantage?

4 Try to explain why a sphere has the lowest surface area of any shape for a given volume.

Quarrying RCKS

Digging out the rock

The photograph shows a quarry where rock is being mined. The quarry covers a large area. Mining rocks makes a lot of noise and dust. The rocks are often broken up with explosives, and large excavators are used to load rocks into lorries. These lorries may need to carry their loads along narrow roads.

Using rocks

We need these rocks for all sorts of uses. Much of the quarried rock is used to build and repair roads, to support railway lines, and to make foundations for buildings. Most rock is used within 50 km of where it is quarried.

Limestone is a particularly useful rock. It can be converted to an alkali. It is used for making all sorts of things, including cement, iron and steel, medicines, plastics, cosmetics, paint, sugar, glass, and paper.

Did You Know?

Limestone is mainly calcium carbonate. It was formed millions of years ago from the remains of creatures that lived in the sea.

Key
- granite
- slate
- limestone
- chalk

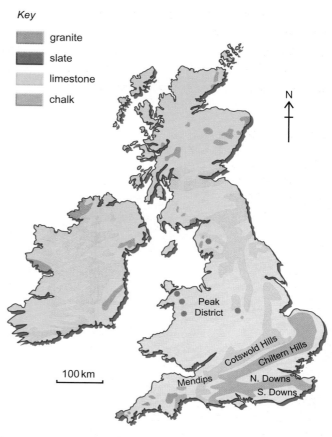

The map shows the rocks quarried in different parts of the United Kingdom.

1 Would you want a quarry near your home? Why?

2 Why do you think most rock is used close to where it is quarried?

3 Find out which rocks are quarried near you.

4 Limestone is used in power stations to remove acidic gases from the waste gases. Why are the acidic gases removed?

Limestone mining in the PEAK DISTRICT

The Peak District National Park

The photograph and map show the Peak District National Park, an area of natural beauty.

- Mining and quarrying have been carried out in the area for centuries.

- At present 4 million tonnes of limestone are minted here each year. Of this 2.4 million tonnes are used for road-making materials and 1.6 million tonnes are used for making steel, cement, and other chemical uses.

- Smaller quarries in the area produce 60 000 tonnes of sandstone, which is used as a building material.

- The mineral fluorspar (calcium fluoride) is also mined, which is used in various products including refrigerants, solvents, aerosols, and anaesthetics.

- Small amounts of other rocks and minerals are also mined.

- The Peak District Park is the second most visited National Park in the world, with 20 million visitors each year. It is close to the large cities of Sheffield, Huddersfield, Stoke-on-Trent, Derby, and Leicester.

- The National Park is not owned by the Government. Most of the land is privately owned.

- If a mining company wants to quarry in the area, they first ask permission from the Peak Park authorities. If they have permission, they pay the landowner for the right to mine.

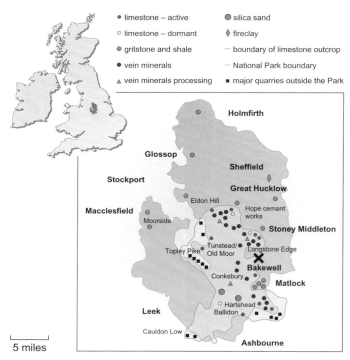

- limestone – active
- limestone – dormant
- gritstone and shale
- vein minerals
- vein minerals processing
- silica sand
- fireclay
- — boundary of limestone outcrop
- — National Park boundary
- ■ major quarries outside the Park

5 miles

A mining company wants to open a large new mine at the position marked X on the map

100

Alice is a retired old age pensioner living in the south of England. She has some shares in the mining company.

Jerry and Anne live with their two young children in Bakewell. They both work in Bakewell. The children go to local schools. They hope the children will grow up and live in the area.

Dave lives in the Peak District and is a lorry driver. He is currently unemployed.

Ali and Shareen have a small business in Sheffield and like to take their children for days out into the Peak District.

Kath and Alan run a small shop in the Peak District which is popular with visitors for drinks and snacks.

Graham and Liz own the land where the large company wants to mine.

1 Put yourself in the position of each of the people shown. For each, write a paragraph explaining their views on the proposed mining.

2 Make a list of advantages and a list of disadvantages of the proposed mining scheme.

Make a decision about whether it should go ahead. Support your decision by explaining your reasons.

Weathering

The rocks on the surface of the Earth are continually broken down by the joint attack of the air, surface water, and solar radiation. The rocks are **weathered** – they are worn away where they stand. The rocks are broken down into small particles.

There are three main types of weathering – mechanical, chemical, and biological.

Mechanical weathering

Rocks are physically broken down into smaller pieces, but they are not changed chemically. Alternate heating and cooling makes the rocks expand and contract. This produces stresses in the rocks which cause them to break up. Ice forms in the cracks in the rock. Water expands as it freezes, so the ice pushes the rock apart.

Biological weathering

As plant roots grow into or under rocks, they can cause stresses and strains on the rocks. They can make cracks larger and cause rocks to split.

This concrete path (above) has been cracked by tree roots. Lichens and mosses that grow on stone (right) slowly eat away the rocks on which they grow. This is an example of biological weathering.

Chemical weathering

Rocks are attacked by acids in the atmosphere, by water, and by oxygen. A series of reactions may break down the rock. Oxidation, hydration, and hydrolysis reactions may be involved. For example, rainwater contains dissolved carbon dioxide which forms carbonic acid. Carbonic acid can react with limestone forming calcium hydrogencarbonate.

Granite contains many minerals including quartz, feldspar, and mica. Quartz resists chemical weathering but feldspar and mica are broken down to form clay materials. The granite crumbles away.

> ### Did You Know?
> Weathering is usually a very slow process, taking hundreds of years to affect a rock even slightly.

1 What are the three types of weathering?

2 Why do you think there are more lichens growing on stonework in country districts than in towns?

3 Write word equations for the reactions which cause limestone (calcium carbonate) to break down by chemical weathering.

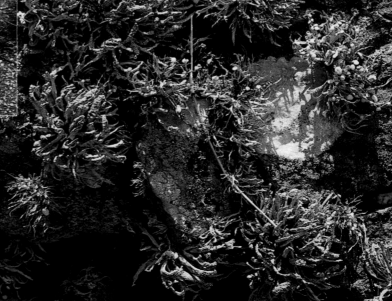

Cement and concrete

John Smeaton's lighthouse, that now stands in Plymouth

The Eddystone lighthouse stands on the treacherous Eddystone rocks close to Plymouth. There have been four lighthouses here in the last 400 years. The most famous one, the third one, was built by John Smeaton, often called the world's first civil engineer. He used a quick-setting and water-resistant cement which set underwater to join the massive blocks of stone together. The cement had a high lime content which helped it set quickly. This lighthouse survived the ravages of the sea for 117 years before it was re-erected on Plymouth Hoe as a memorial to John Smeaton.

Today cement is a common building material. There are many types of cement for special purposes.

This concrete bridge spans the River Ichen in Southampton

Making cement

Cement is made by grinding limestone, sand, and clay together and then heating the mixture. The heating is done in a rotary kiln 160 m long. A chemical change takes place, forming a mixture of calcium silicate and aluminium silicate. This is cement. The temperature rises to 1000 °C during the reaction.

When a builder adds water to cement, various reactions take place, producing calcium hydroxide. This absorbs carbon dioxide, and the cement sets. Long crystals of calcium carbonate are formed which give strength to the cement. Cement is used as mortar to join bricks, or to make concrete.

Making concrete

Cement is mixed with sand, small stones, and water to produce concrete. Concrete is used to build all sorts of structures, from garden ornaments to office blocks and bridges.

Did You Know?

Lime-based concrete has been known for 7000 years. The Romans made good cement for their many buildings. After the fall of the Roman Empire, cement-making was not so successful again until the seventeenth century.

In 1824, a bricklayer called Joseph Aspidin invented Portland cement, which looks like Portland stone when it hardens. Both Aspidin and John Smeaton came from Leeds.

1　What materials are used to make cement?

2　Cement and concrete are not very strong materials. What can be done to make them stronger?

SHALES

What are shales?

About three-quarters of the surface rocks of the Earth are sedimentary. Of these approximately 12% are sandstones and 8% are limestones. The rest are **shales**.

The particles in shales came from the weathering of silicates in igneous rocks. Fine-grained particles were produced which were carried by water and deposited as mud. The layers of mud turned slowly to shale over thousands of years.

This black shale contains fossils

Did You Know?

Alum was extracted from shale using human urine. In 1770, 3000 tonnes of alum were produced. It took the urine of over 1000 people to do this.

Shales and alum

Shales are used for many purposes, including making bricks and ceramic products and in paint pigments. One important chemical extracted from shales is alum. This was used to soften leather. It was also used when dyeing wool with natural dyes. It **fixed** the dye to the wool.

In 1856 William Perkin discovered a synthetic dye by accident. He made a purple substance which would dye silk. This was the start of the synthetic dyes industry. Since then the demand for alum has been greatly reduced, because synthetic dyes do not need to be fixed.

There are several different alums.

- Potassium alum is potassium aluminium sulphate, $K_2SO_4.Al_2(SO_4)_3.24H_2O$.

- Ammonium alum is aluminium ammonium sulphate, $(NH_4)_2SO_4.Al_2(SO_4)_3.24H_2O$.

This black shale contains crude oil

Shales and crude oil

Shales are important today because crude oil is present in many black shales. The oil is extracted by heating the black shale out of contact with air.

1 What percentage of the surface rocks of the Earth are sedimentary rocks?

2 What percentage of the surface sedimentary rocks are shales?

3 What are the five elements present in potassium alum?

4 Why do you think it is important to keep air out when black shale is heated to extract crude oil?

Wool has its dye fixed by alum

The river breaks off pieces of rocks, carries them, and then deposits them lower down the valley

Erosion

Weathering is the breaking down of rocks into small fragments where they stand. Erosion is the breaking down of rocks by moving air, water, or particles. Erosion is constantly changing the appearance of rocks. There are four major causes of erosion – rivers, ice, sea, and wind.

Rivers

Fast-flowing rivers cut into valleys. Moving water carries tremendous potential energy. Rivers can cut their way through rocks and when the river slows down, much of this rock is then deposited. The photograph shows a river flowing through a valley.

Ice

At times in history the Earth was much colder, and much of Britain was covered with ice sheets. These ice sheets moved slowly over the land, wearing away the rocks as they went. Much of the material produced by this erosion formed the clay that covers much of southern and eastern England.

The sea

Just as a river can wear away rocks, so can the constant movement of the sea. However, the sea can erode the landscape much faster. Chalk cliffs in East Sussex are eroding at the rate of 1 m each year. Material produced by this erosion is deposited elsewhere along the coast.

The wind

The wind can cause erosion. In the desert, sand is blown around by the wind. This can erode rocks by 'sandblasting'.

The Sphinx in Egypt has been eroded over the centuries by the wind blowing sand at it

Did You Know?

A river flowing at 24 km/h can move boulders with a mass greater than 1 tonne.

1 What are the four things which cause erosion?

2 The speed at which a river erodes rocks depends upon various factors. Suggest factors that might affect this speed.

GRAVEYARD TRIP

You are going to visit a local graveyard and carry out a survey of gravestones. Back at school you can process the data you have collected.

Planning your test

First you should have a **hypothesis** to test. Here are some examples.

1 Granite is more resistant to weathering than other rocks.

2 Mosses and lichens grow better on north-facing sides of gravestones.

3 More mosses and lichens grow on granite than on marble.

Your teacher might suggest other hypotheses for you to test depending upon the graveyard you visit.

Identifying rocks

You might use a key like the one on the right to identify samples of rocks in the laboratory before your visit. You can then compare the samples with the gravestones.

The visit

Remember that other people may be at the graveyard. They may be visiting the graves of relatives. Do respect other people, and do not clamber over graves or make a lot of noise.

First make a sketch map of the graveyard showing any features such as gates, a place of worship, tall trees, etc. Mark the direction of north on your map. Then start to collect data. Copy the table below. Look at gravestones and record the information in the table.

Processing your data

When you return to school you will have to process the data you have collected. Your teacher may suggest you share data with other pupils.

The diagram shows two ways of processing the data about types of stone. You may be able to think of others. Make sure you process the data in a way that helps test your hypothesis.

You may wish to use a computer to help you process the data.

Key for identifying rock samples

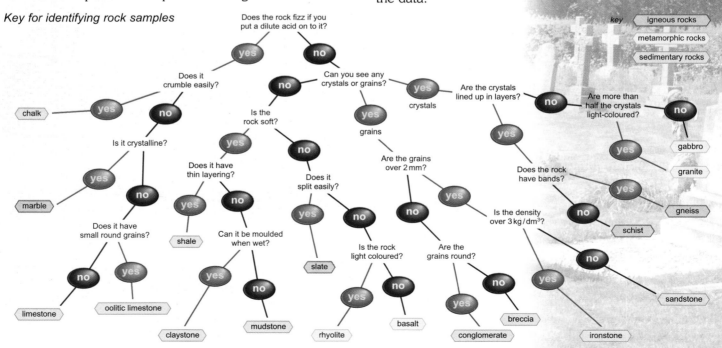

Surname on grave	Date of burial (use earliest date if more than one)	Type of stone such as granite (see key)	Amount of weathering (high, medium, low)	Which direction does the grave-stone face?	Is the gravestone under trees?	Is there moss or lichen on the stone? If so, how much? Which direction does that side of the stone face?

Types of stone used in the graveyard

number of headstones

granite marble sandstone slate

Types of stone used in the graveyard

granite / sandstone — up to 1800

marble / granite / sandstone — 1801–1900

slate / marble / granite / sandstone — 1901 to present day

Microelectronic
SYSTEMS

Electrical, electronic, or microelectronic?

In an **electrical system**, electricity is used to provide heating, lighting, or movement, or a combination of these. The system can be switched on and off by mechanical switches operated by fingers or relays. There may be time-delay switches that are operated by a clockwork mechanism. Lamps and toasters are examples of electrical systems.

Electronic systems are more complex. They include an electronic circuit that processes information in some way.

Which is electrical and which is microelectronic?

The first electronic processors were based on vacuum tubes, or **valves**, and they had very limited processing power compared with a desk-top computer of today. Systems became smaller following the invention of the transistor in 1948. Suddenly portable radios were possible. In the 1960s, every teenager had to have one! Nowadays hundreds of thousands of transistors and other components can be built into a single integrated circuit, commonly called a microchip. This is the world of **microelectronics.**

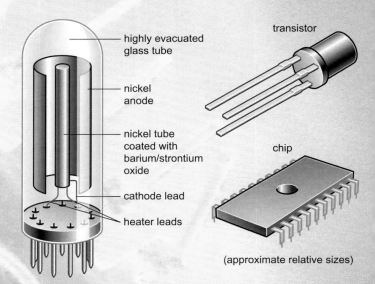

highly evacuated glass tube

nickel anode

nickel tube coated with barium/strontium oxide

cathode lead

heater leads

transistor

chip

(approximate relative sizes)

Electronic systems have become smaller and smaller as technology has advanced. The valve was replaced by the transistor and then the microchip which contains many thousands of transistors.

 1 List six examples of electrical systems and six examples of microelectronic systems.

You may find it easy to think of six examples of microelectronic systems, but more difficult to think of six electrical systems. A vacuum cleaner used to be a simple electrical system, consisting of a switch and a motor with the necessary wiring. A modern-day vacuum cleaner has sensors so it can recognize how deep the pile is on a carpet, and even how dirty the carpet is, and then make adjustments to the speed of the motor.

A microelectronic system in detail

Each photograph on the right shows a microelectronic system. All microelectronic systems have three things in common – an **input**, a **processor**, and an **output**. The input provides information to the processor. The processor makes a decision based on this information and passes instructions on to the output device.

A complex system such as a microcomputer may have several input and output devices. The most basic machine has a keyboard and mouse to input information, a processor to process the information, and a monitor to output the information after it has been processed.

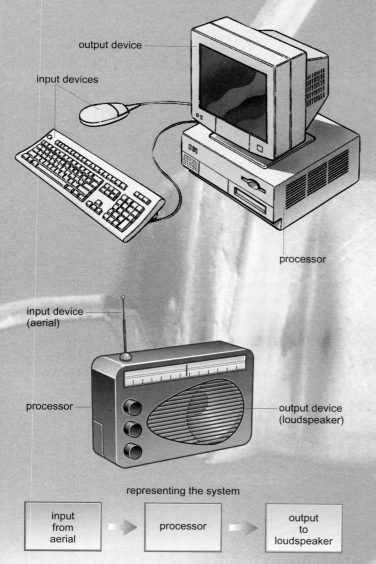

output device

input devices

processor

input device
(aerial)

processor

output device
(loudspeaker)

representing the system

input from aerial	processor	output to loudspeaker

2 Your teacher will give you an advert from a computer magazine. Design your own microelectronic system. Choose a processor, an input device, and an output device. Work to a budget of £1000 altogether.

3 Identify the input device or devices and the output device or devices for each of the following systems. Draw a diagram like the one for the radio to represent each system.

a a television

b the computer that you designed in question **2**

c a burglar alarm

d a portable telephone

- The diagram on the left shows how a radio can be thought of as a microelectronic system.

- The aerial inputs information. It detects radio waves and produces a small varying voltage.

- This information is then processed in the radio. The processor produces a larger varying voltage that represents the sound.

- The loudspeaker outputs the information. It uses this varying voltage to produce a sound.

Experimenting with
SYSTEMS

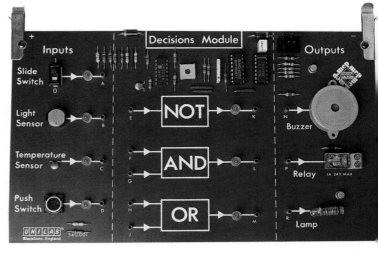

Going digital

Modern electronics and communications systems are **digital**. This means that they handle information that is represented as a number, usually in binary form. **Binary numbers** use only two digits, 1 and 0. In the microelectronic systems that you study in this unit, 0 represents 'off' and 1 represents 'on'.

Inputs and outputs

The photograph shows a decisions board. You can use a board like this to experiment by making microelectronics systems that carry out specific tasks.

Sensor	Condition	Signal (0 or 1)
slide switch	up	
	down	
light sensor	light	
	dark	
temperature sensor	cold	
	warm	
push switch	not pushed	
	pushed	

On the left-hand side it has four input devices. In the middle of the board there are three processors. On the right of the board are the three output devices.

The four input devices are

- a slide switch
- a press switch
- a light sensor
- a temperature sensor.

You can also use a remote sensor if you want to use a sensor that is not fixed to the board, for example to sense the temperature outside. Each sensor can give one of two signals – either 0 or 1. A light-emitting diode (LED) by each sensor shows its signal. When the LED is lit, the sensor is giving the signal 1. When the LED is unlit, the signal is 0.

Activity

Check the signal from each sensor for its two conditions.

Copy the table and complete it to record your results.

The processors

The three processors, or **logic gates**, on the decisions board are called **NOT**, **AND**, and **OR**. You will learn the reasons for these names when you have experimented with them. The NOT gate has one input socket, and the others have two. These input sockets receive information from the sensors when they are linked. The LED at the right-hand side of each processor shows its decision or output.

The next photograph shows how to link two sensors, the slide switch and push switch, to the input of the OR gate.

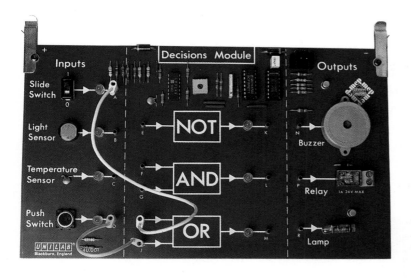

Telling the truth

Whether the output of a logic gate is 0 or 1 depends on the input or inputs to the gate. A **truth table** is a table that shows the output for all the possible input combinations. The NOT gate has only two possible inputs, 0 or 1. There are four possible combinations for the AND gate and the OR gate.

Activity

For each gate, copy its truth table below. Complete it by filling in the output (0 or 1) for each set of inputs shown in the table.

NOT	
Input	Output
0	
1	

AND		
Inputs		Output
0	0	
1	0	
0	1	
1	1	

OR		
Inputs		Output
0	0	
1	0	
0	1	
1	1	

 1 For each gate, explain what inputs you need for the output to be 1. Why do the gates have the names they do?

111

timer

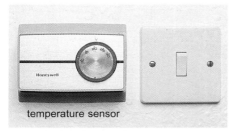

temperature sensor

The boiler turns on if the room is cold and if the timer is on

The output devices

The processor, or logic gate, makes a decision according to the information it receives from the input devices. It can then communicate this decision to an output device. For example, the processor in a central heating system receives information from the temperature sensor (and probably from a timer as well). If the room is warm enough, the output to the heater is 0, but if it is too cold the output is 1 to turn the heater on.

The three output devices on the decisions board are

- a lamp

- a buzzer

- a relay.

The lamp produces a signal that you can see, and the buzzer makes a sound that you can hear. The relay is an electromagnetic switch. This can be used to switch on other devices such as a heater or a refrigerator compressor.

A complete system

The photograph below shows a complete microelectronics system. It has two input devices, a processor, and an output. The input devices are the push switch and the slide switch. They feed to the input of the processor, the OR gate. The decision made by the processor is the output. This goes to an output device, the buzzer.

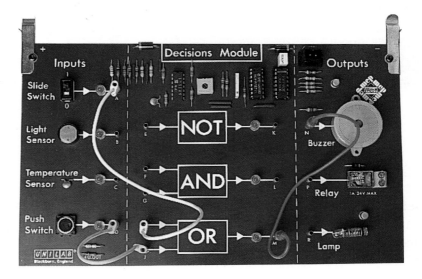

Designing systems to carry out tasks

An incubator is a container kept at a steady temperature, for example to hatch eggs. An incubator uses a microelectronic system to control the temperature inside. The system needs to switch on a heater when the incubator is too cold, and switch it off when the incubator is warm.

To design a system for an incubator, you need to choose an input device (or devices), a processor, and an output device. The only input you need to detect is temperature, so the temperature sensor is used as the input device. The output device is the incubator heater, which will be switched on or off by the relay on the decisions board.

What would happen if you used the temperature sensor to switch the heater on and off directly? Unfortunately it would switch the heater on when the incubator was warm, and keep the heater off when the incubator was cold. Using the NOT processor between the temperature sensor and the heater solves this problem. The system is shown in the diagram.

In an incubator, the temperature is kept constant by turning a heater on and off

Activity
Make the system shown on the left and check that it does the job correctly.

| temperature sensor | → | NOT | → | relay | → | heater |

This truth table shows the input and output for the two input conditions cold and warm.

Temperature sensor	Input to NOT gate	Output from NOT gate	Heater on or off
cold	0	1	on
warm	1	0	off

2 Design a microelectronic system that turns on a fan if the air temperature is too warm. The fan only needs to operate during daylight. Base your system around the AND gate. Draw a system diagram of your solution like the one on the left. Then build the system. Test it with the four possible sets of inputs.

3 Design a burglar alarm that sounds a buzzer if either one of two doors is opened. Each door is fitted with a switch. Use the push switch and the slide switch as input devices.

4 Design a microelectronics system that lights a warning lamp if the inside of a refrigerator becomes too warm when the door has been left open.

Designing complex
SYSTEMS

The logic gates AND, NOT, and OR can act as processors in microelectronic systems. In more complex processors, two or more of these gates are used together.

AND

NOT

OR

Combining gates

To show how gates are combined, you can use circuit symbols to represent the gates. The circuit symbols for AND, NOT, and OR are shown on the left. In each case the lines on the left are the inputs and the line on the right is the output.

You can combine gates by connecting the output of one gate to the input of another. The photograph shows the slide switch and push switch connected to the input of the AND gate. The output from the AND gate then goes to the input of the NOT gate. This is shown in the circuit diagram below.

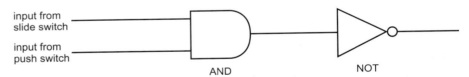

input from slide switch

input from push switch

AND

NOT

An AND gate followed by a NOT gate makes a NAND gate

Activity

Build the circuit shown in the circuit diagram. Copy and complete the truth table below to show the outputs for all possible inputs.

?

1 Describe how the output of the NOT gate depends on the inputs to the AND gate.

2 Describe the relationship between the output from the NAND gate and its inputs. Why does the gate have the name NAND?

NAND

This combination of two gates, an AND followed by an OR, is called a **NAND** gate. NAND stands for NOTAND.

Input		AND gate output	NOT gate output
Slide switch	Push switch		
O	O		
1	O		
O	1		
1	1		

NOR

The circuit diagram below shows how to make a **NOR** gate. This is an OR gate followed by a NOT gate.

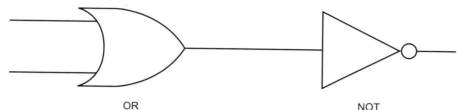

OR   NOT

A NOR gate is made up of an OR gate followed by a NOT gate

> ### Activity
> Build a circuit using a NOR gate, with inputs from the slide switch and the push switch. Copy the truth table below and complete it for all possible inputs.

 3 Describe the relationship between the output from the NOR gate and its inputs. Why does the gate have the name NOR?

Useful combinations

The NAND and NOR gates are particularly useful because it is possible to make AND, NOT, and OR gates just by using NAND or NOR gates connected in different ways. A complex logic gate circuit can be built using only one type of gate.

The following problems can be solved by using either a NAND gate or a NOR gate.

 4 Design a system to switch on a greenhouse fan heater on cold nights.

5 Design a system that switches a storage heater. The heater should always be switched on at night, but only be switched on during the day in cold weather.

Input		AND gate output	NOT gate output
Slide switch	Push switch		
0	0		
1	0		
0	1		
1	1		

Commercial greenhouses have systems to control watering, ventilation, and temperature

Other combinations

Early cropping rhubarb is 'forced' by growing it in a warm dark shed. A system sounds a warning buzzer if the shed becomes cold or light or both.

The truth table shows the output needed for the four possible inputs from a temperature sensor and a light sensor.

| Input | | Output (buzzer) |
Temperature sensor	Light sensor	
0	0	1
0	1	1
1	0	0
1	1	1

The conditions for growing early rhubarb are controlled by a microelectronic system

None of the five logic gates you have looked at produces the outputs shown in the truth table. However, if the buzzer needed to sound if it was warm or light or both, instead of cold or light or both, the OR gate would give the desired output. So as well as the OR gate, we can use the NOT gate to invert the signal from the temperature sensor, so that a 0 becomes a 1 and a 1 becomes a 0. The circuit diagram is shown on the right.

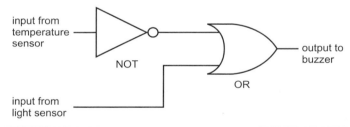

6   Copy the truth table below for this circuit. Complete it and check that it does the required job.

7   Design a system to operate a heater so that it is only switched on if it is cold during the day.

| Input to NOT gate | Input to OR gate | | Output to buzzer |
	From NOT gate	From light sensor	
0		0	
0		1	
1		0	
1		1	

Course Summaries

Biology

Life processes and cell activity

- Life is a set of co-ordinated processes. There are seven processes which all living things perform:

  respiration - releasing energy;

  excretion - getting rid of waste;

  nutrition - getting food, water and minerals;

  sensitivity - responding to changes;

  movement - change of position;

  reproduction - making more individuals of the same sort.

- Some living things like viruses may have evolved from living things even though they no longer have all the processes of life.

- All living things also have a **DNA/RNA** blueprint and most have **cells.**

- All plants and animals are made from cells.

- All cells have a **nucleus, cytoplasm,** and **cell membrane.** The nucleus is the control centre which holds the DNA (blueprint). The cell membrane controls what comes into and out of cells. The cytoplasm is where the cell carries out most of its reactions.

- Most cells also have **vacuoles** where they store things.

- Plant cells also have a **cell wall** and may also have **chloroplasts**. The cell wall helps hold the plant up and is fully permeable. The chloroplast is where food is made (**photosynthesis**).

- Multicellular organisms have specialist cells. Specialist cells are adapted for particular jobs e.g. windpipe lining cells are regular and have hairs on which help get rid of dust trapped in mucus.

- Groups of similar specialist cells are called a **tissue** e.g. muscle tissue. **Organs** are structures made from several tissues to perform particular jobs e.g. the heart. Tissues and organs are built into **systems** which work together for an overall function e.g. the digestive system. All systems work together to form a healthy **organism.**

Humans as organisms

- People need **fats**, **proteins**, **carbohydrates**, **vitamins**, **minerals**, **water**, and **fibre**. Carbohydrates (CHO) are the fuel for energy release through respiration. Fats (CHO) provide energy; insulation and the basis of the cell membrane. Proteins (CHON) make enzymes, muscles and many cell structures (growth and repair). Vitamins (A, B, C, D, E) mostly work to help enzymes function. Water is needed to replace that lost each day. Fibre helps food get absorbed and pass through the gut

- All the things we take in are our **diet**. Things are needed in exact amounts depending on our growth rate and activity levels – this is a **balanced diet.**

- Food molecules are large and need to be digested to make them small enough to be taken in. Digestion is aided by **enzymes** – biological catalysts that speed up reactions. Enzymes are proteins that work because of their shape. Things we eat are either **absorbed** or **egested** (passed out). Once in the body the small food molecules can be rebuilt into whatever we need.

- **Blood** carries materials around the body e.g. food from the gut to the cells. Blood carries a fluid (**plasma**) and **red** and **white cells.**

- The **heart** is a double pump which drives blood round the boy in a **double circulation**. The right heart drives blood to the lungs to pick up oxygen. The left heart sends blood round the rest of the body. **Valves** in the heart control the direction of the flow. **Arteries** are muscular tubes which carry blood under pressure away from the heart. **Veins** are thin walled vessels with valves which carry blood back to the heart. **Capillaries** link the arteries and veins and allow materials to be passed to and from the tissues.

- The skeleton is jointed for movement. It also protects organs in the body e.g. the skull protects the brain.

- There are different types of joint in the skeleton. A see-saw joint under the skull allows the head to tip from side to side. Wheelbarrow joint in the ankle supports the body weight. Hinge joints at elbow and knees allow flexible movement.

Course Summaries

- Muscles only contract by themselves – they have to be pulled back out, therefore muscles work in pairs (**antagonists**) which pull in opposite directions.

- Humans reproduce sexually (they have male and female sex cells – **gametes**). Males produce **sperm** fed and protected by **semen**. Females ripen and release an **egg** once a month from the ovaries.

- The lining of the womb grows and is shed monthly linked to the production of the egg – this is the **menstrual cycle**

- Sperm may meet the egg in the fallopian tube (**oviduct**) where one will enter the egg (**fertilization**).

- Fertilizsed eggs attach to the womb lining and grow into it to form a **placenta.**

- The egg grows by **cell division** getting food from the mother through the placenta and passing wastes back to the mother the same way.

- The early stages of development are called the embryo but once the baby looks fully human it is called a foetus.

- These functions develop in **adolescence** and are accompanied by other body changes: hair grows under the arms and around the genitals; girls develop breasts, broader hips, and the menstrual cycle; boys get facial hair, broader shoulders, and stronger muscles.

- The breathing system is made of the windpipe (**trachea**); the bronchi; the bronchioles and **alveoli** both of which are found in the lungs.

- The breathing tubes are supported by cartilage rings to stop them collapsing under the pressure changes. They are lined by cells with tiny hairs (**cilia**) which move the mucus which traps dust away from the lungs.

- Alveoli have thin walls and a good blood supply to enable oxygen to be absorbed and carbon dioxide to be got rid of.

- The lungs are held in an airtight pack by the ribs, the pleural membranes and the **diaphragm.**

- The ribs and diaphragm move to make the chest larger or smaller. Air is forced in by atmospheric pressure or pushed out by muscular pressure

- Smoking causes tar to line the lungs which stops the cilia working. Nicotine from cigarettes is an addictive drug. Smoking increases the risk of death from a number of causes e.g. lung cancer.

- **Respiration** is a process in every cell which releases energy from food. Mostly oxygen is used to burn (oxidise) the food – **aerobic respiration**:

  food + oxygen = energy + carbon dioxide + water

  Sometimes the food is broken down without oxygen – **anaerobic respiration.**

- **Fermentation** is one form of respiration which produces alcohol e.g. in yeast. Another form used by people produces lactic acid in muscles which eventually causes cramp.

- Good health is about the body and mind working together to maintain the whole organism.

- Disease is caused by **microbes** (mainly bacteria and viruses) attacking the cells of the body and killing them. The body has external defences – oily skin, mucus in the lungs and nose, earwax, blood clotting; internal defences; – white blood cells which eat germs, white blood cells that produce chemicals (anti toxins) that destroy the germs.

- **Vaccination** can help by developing the immune system without getting the disease.

- Medical drugs can help by curing diseases by killing germs (e.g. antibiotics) or by alleviating pain (e.g. Aspirin). Other drugs may create a sense of pleasure but all damage the body and make it less healthy e.g. alcohol kills brain cells.

- Exercise keeps you healthy.

Green plants as organisms

- Plants make food from water and carbon dioxide using energy from the Sun. **Chlorophyll** acts as an energy transducer to turn the suns energy into chemical energy:

  carbon dioxide + water (with chlorophyll) + Sun's energy = sugar + oxygen

Course Summaries

- The sugar is turned into fats and proteins as well and the plants need minerals (especially nitrogen for this to happen). Oxygen is a waste product. Plants need other minerals for healthy growth. Root hair cells take in water and minerals from the soil.

- Flowers are designed to reproduce sexually (they have male and female sex cells).

- **Pollen** (contains the male sex cells) is made in the anther of the stamen. It is transferred from the **anther** to the **stigma** by wind or insects.

- Wind pollinated plants have long **stamens**; lots of light pollen; feathery stigmas; small dull **petals.**

- Insect pollinated plants have large sticky pollen grains; sticky stigmas; stout parts to prevent breakage; bright petals. Eggs are made in the **ovule. Pollen tubes** grow into the ovule and fertilisation occurs there producing a seed.

- Seeds are dispersed by wind; animals; mechanically; or by water.

- All plants respire all the time. During the day energy is also released by photosynthesis so plants do not respire much during daylight. How much oxygen is used or given out depends on the balance between photosynthesis and respiration. The same is true for carbon dioxide uptake and release.

Variation, classification, and inheritance

- There are millions of different living things – each one is called a **species.** Members of each species have key features in common. Members of each species also differ in a number of ways – this is called variation. Some variation is **inherited** and some is caused by the **environment.** Some variation is **continuous** (e.g. height – any measurement could be found). Some variation is **discontinuous** (e.g. tongue rolling – you either can or can't, there are no in-beweens).

- Species are grouped (classified) to help us cope with the large numbers and to try to reflect how they are related to evolution.

- Species are grouped into **genera** (singular genus); genera into **families**; families into **orders**; orders into **classes**; classes into **phyla** and phyla into **kingdoms**: a kingdom is a major style of living e.g. moving and eating (animals), making food and staying put (plants); a phylum is a major body plan within a kingdom e.g. arthropods, chordates.

- A **key** is a tool to help you identify a specimen you have found.

- Sexual reproduction leads to variation within a species. Some variants survive better than other because they are better fitted to the environment around them. As long as they breed more of their type will appear in the next generation. This process is called **natural selection** and leads to species changing (evolving). By choosing which organisms to breed we can produce a similar process in animals and plants we use (e.g. pet dogs) – this process is called **artificial selection.**

Living things in their environment

- The world is divided into major regions of vegetation controlled by climate – these are **biomes** (e.g. deciduous woodland).

- Biomes contain **ecosystems** – more or less limited areas in which all the organisms are interlinked (e.g. a pond).

- All living things need a **habitat** which provides enough food; a place to breed; and a place to shelter.

- Organisms are **adapted** to their particular ecosystem and habitat (e.g. a woodpecker has a specially designed tongue and skull to get insect food from inside tress; bluebells flower early to avoid being shaded by the trees when their leaves come out).

- Many adaptations are based on seasonal changes (e.g. migration).

- Organisms feed on each other and these links form **food chains.** All food chains start with a plant (**producer**) which gets energy from the Sun. All other links are **consumers** – some are **herbivores** (plant eaters) and some are **carnivores** (animal eaters). Most food chains are short because much is wasted in transfer between each link.

- Food chains can be represented in a **food web** where each organism is only shown once.

- Any poisons that accumulate in bodies get more concentrated as you pass along a food chain – this can cause real problems for top predators.

- All living things die and get **recycled** by **decomposers.**

- Populations grow in an 'S' shaped fashion – initial exponential phase, a plateau phase, a degeneration phase: The plateau stage is called the **carrying capacity**; the carrying capacity depends on the food availability; space; competition for resources; predation. Competition can be between species or within a species. Within a species the ones that compete more successfully will usually produce more offspring in the next generation.

Chemistry

Classifying materials

- Matter can exist in three states depending upon **temperature** and **pressure**. The three states are: solid, liquid, and gas. The diagrams show the arrangement of particles.

solid	liquid	gas

In a solid (except ice) the particles are tightly linked together and can only vibrate.

In a liquid the particles are slightly freer to move than in a solid.

In a gas the particles are moving rapidly with no pattern to their movement (random).

- The pressure of a gas is caused by collisions of particles with the wall of the container. The more collisions the higher the pressure. The particles in a gas move to fill all of the available space. This is called diffusion.

- Matter is made up from about 100 elements. A pure element is made up of very tiny particles called atoms. Elements can be represented by symbols ,e.g. **C carbon** , **Mg magnesium** , **O oxygen**. The **periodic table** is a chart which shows al the elements.

- **Elements** combine together in chemical reactions to form compounds. A **compound**, e.g. water, has a definite composition and properties different from the elements that make it up. Water can be represented by a formula, H_2O

- Elements can be divided into **metals** and **non-metals**. Metals are usually shiny solids at room temperature. Most are good conductors of heat and electricity.

- **Mixtures**, e.g. air, sea water do not have a definite composition. The different components of the mixture are not combined.

- Methods such as filtration, distillation, fractional distillation, and chromatography can be used to separate mixtures.

- Non-metals can be solid, liquid, or gas at room temperature and atmospheric pressure. They are poor conductors of heat and electricity.

Changing materials

- Changes can be **physical** or **temporary changes** (such as melting, freezing, boiling, condensing, or dissolving) or **chemical** or **permanent changes** (such as rusting, burning, reaction with acid).

- In a physical change, there is no mass lost or gained during the change. In a chemical reaction, again there is no mass loss providing the total masses of reactants and products are compared.

- Different substances **change state** at different temperatures. Melting and freezing take place at the melting (or freezing) point. Boiling and condensing take place at the boiling point. Energy is released when liquids freeze and gases condense. Energy is taken in from the surrounding when solids melt or liquids boil.

- The **solubility** of most solid solutes in water increases with rising temperature. However, the solubility of gases is much less and this decreases with rising temperature.

- Rocks are broken down or **weathered** by repeated changes in temperature causing the rock to expand and contract. If water is trapped in cracks in the rock it expands when it freezes, forcing the rock to split apart.

Course Summaries

- Rocks can be divided into **igneous** rocks, **sedimentary** rocks, and **metamorphic** rocks. Igneous rocks, such as granite and basalt, are formed when molten magma from inside the Earth cools and crystallises.

- Sedimentary rocks such as limestone and sandstone are formed when small exiting fragments of rock settle in water and are compressed and cemented together.

- Metamorphic rocks, such as marble, are formed when high temperatures and/or high pressures act on sedimentary rocks.

- Rocks from the Earth are recycled to form new rocks in the **rock cycle**.

- Nearly all materials are made from one or more chemical reactions.

- A chemical reaction can be represented by a **word equation**. There are useful chemical reactions (extracting iron from iron ore or burning natural gas) and ones that are not useful (souring of milk or rusting of iron).

- There are different **types of reaction** including combustion, decomposition, and oxidation. Energy transfers occur in chemical reactions, e.g. burning fossil fuels. This transfer of energy can be controlled and used.

Patterns of behaviour

- Metals often **react with oxygen**, water, and acid.

    A metal reacting with oxygen forms an oxide.

    e.g. copper + oxygen → copper oxide

- If a metal **reacts with water** it forms hydrogen gas and leaves an alkaline residue.

    e.g. sodium + hydrogen → sodium hydroxide + hydrogen

- When a fairly reactive metal **reacts with dilute acid** it formed a salt and hydrogen.

    metal + acid → salt + hydrogen

- Using the results of reactions with air, water, and acid, metals can be arranged in **order of reactivity**. This is called a **reactivity series** and the most reactive metal is at the top and the least reactive at the bottom.

- If a metal is placed in a solution of a salt containing a less reactive metal, a **displacement reaction** takes place.

    e.g. iron + copper(II) sulphate → iron(II) sulphate + copper

- The reactivity series can be used to make predictions about reactions which take place.

- The acidity or alkalinity of a solution can be found using indicators such as Universal indicator. The **pH value** can be measured and a pH value of 7 means neutral. A pH value less than 7 shows an acid and one greater than 7 an alkali.

- Acids react with metals, metal oxides, metal hydroxides, or metal carbonates to form salts. Sulphuric acid forms sulphates. Hydrochloric acid forms chlorides and nitric acid forms nitrates. The reaction of an acid and an alkali is called neutralisation.

- Acids in the atmosphere can lead to corrosion of metals or chemical weathering of rocks.

Physics

Electricity and magnetism

- Charge that is not moving is called **static charge**. All objects can carry static charge, but conductors need to be well insulated to prevent the charge from passing through them to the Earth.

- **Insulators** are easily charged by rubbing against another material. The friction forces cause electrons to be transferred from one material to the other. The material that gains electrons becomes negatively charged and the material that loses electrons becomes positively charged.

- Charged objects exert forces on other charged objects; those with the same type of charge (both negative or both positive) repel each other while objects with opposite types of charge (one positive and one negative) attract each other.

- Charge flows easily through **conductors** to form an electric current. Current is measured in amps using an **ammeter**.

Course Summaries

- In a **series circuit** there is only one path from the positive terminal of the battery or power supply to the negative terminal. The current in a series circuit is measured by placing an ammeter in series with the electricity source and the circuit components. No matter where it is placed in a series circuit, the ammeter always gives the same reading. This shows that no current is used up by a lamp or other component in the circuit.

- A **parallel circuit** has two or more current paths. Where there is a junction in a parallel circuit, the total current that enters the junction is equal to the total current that leaves the junction.

- All **electric currents** have their own **magnetic field**. A magnetic field is the space around a magnet or electric current where there are forces on magnetic materials such as iron and steel.

- The field due to the electric current in a coil is weak but it becomes much stronger when a piece of iron is placed in the centre of the coil. A coil of wire fitted with an iron core makes an **electromagnet**. The field of an electromagnet can be turned on and off by switching the current in the coil. This makes the electromagnet useful in devices such as electric bells and relays.

- The bell uses an electromagnet to operate a '**make-and-break**' circuit. When the electromagnet is switched on it attracts the iron armature which then breaks the circuit, switching the electromagnet off. The armature moves back and completes the circuit, switching the electromagnet back on. Each time the electromagnet attracts the armature, the hammer strikes the gong.

- A **relay** is a switch that is operated by an electromagnet. When a current passes in the relay coil, the resulting magnetic field of the coil magnetizes the iron core, which in turn attracts an L-shaped armature. The movement of the armature is used to press two switch contacts together. These contacts are used to switch the current in a separate circuit.

- The advantage of a relay is that coil can operate from a low voltage source and only requires a small current, but it can be used to switch high currents and voltages.

Forces and motion

- Whenever there is movement, forces are involved. Forces are needed to accelerate, to brake and to turn a corner.

- There are normally two forces acting on a moving object. One force acts in the direction of motion. In the case of falling object this force is the **Earth's pull** on the object, also called the object's **weight**. For a vehicle moving on a road, the forwards force is the driving force that acts on the wheels.

- The other force that acts on moving objects opposes the motion. **Air resistance** opposes the motion of an object falling towards the ground and water resistance opposes the forwards motion of a swimmer. There are a number of resistive forces, including air resistance, that act on moving vehicles.

- **Friction** is also a resistive force; it opposes slipping and sliding. Friction is useful in brakes, when a cyclist brakes friction opposes the motion of the wheel rim as it slides over the rubber brake block.

- When the forces acting on an object are equal in size and opposite in direction, they are said to be balanced. **Balanced forces** do not change the speed or direction of a moving object. For a car or cyclist to speed up, the driving force must be greater than the resistive force. Slowing down requires a greater resistive force than driving force. An **unbalanced force** is also needed to change the direction of a moving object.

- The speeds of two moving objects can be compared by comparing the times taken to travel the same distance. The object that takes the shorter time has he greater speed.

- To work out a speed, two measurements are needed. These are the distance travelled by an object and the time it took to travel that distance. **Speed** is calculated using the formula: $\text{speed} = \dfrac{\text{distance}}{\text{time}}$

Course Summaries

- **Pressure** is the effect that a force has in cutting or piercing. A large pressure is needed to push a drawing pin into a board, so the tip of the drawing pin has a small surface area. To create a small pressure when walking on soft snow, snowshoes have a large area. Pressure is calculated using the formula:

$$pressure = \frac{force}{area}$$

when the force is in N and the area in m≤ the pressure is in N/m^2 or Pa (Pascal)

- Forces are also used to turn things round. The further away from the pivot that a force acts, the more effective it is in causing rotation. The turning effect of a force is called the moment. It is calculated using the formula:

moment = force × shortest distance to pivot

- When an object is not turning there is no unbalanced moment. This means that any moment that would turn the object in a clockwise direction must be balanced by an equal-size moment acting in an anticlockwise direction. This is known as the principle of moments.

Light and sound

- Light and sound both travel as **waves**. Light travels much faster than sound and, unlike sound, it can travel in a vacuum.

- Light normally travels in **straight lines**; and this is used to explain how we see things and how shadows are formed. A **shadow** is formed when light passes the edges of an obstacle but does not pass through it.

- When light hits an object, some is absorbed and some is reflected. Most objects **reflect light** by scattering it in all directions. When a plane (flat) mirror reflects light the angle between the reflected light and the mirror is equal to the angle between the incident light and the mirror. This causes a **virtual image** to be formed behind the mirror. The virtual image is upright, the same size as the object and the same distance directly behind the mirror as the object is in front of it.

- When light crosses a boundary between two substances there is a change in speed; this is called **refraction**. The change in speed causes a change in wavelength and, unless the direction of the light is at right angles to the boundary, a change in direction. The refraction of light also causes virtual images; when viewed through transparent materials such as water and glass, objects appear to be closer than they really are. As with mirror images, virtual images formed by water and glass are the same way up and same size as the object.

- White light is a mixture of all the colours of the **rainbow**. It can be split up, or **dispersed**, by passing it through a triangular prism. The light changes direction at each face of the prism, the change in direction of blue light being greater than that of red light.

- All the colours of light can be made by mixing together the three **primary colours**: red, green, and blue. The three secondary colours, yellow (red + green), magenta (blue + red) and cyan (blue + green) are produced when overlapping beams of two primary colours shine onto a white screen. If beams of all three primary colours overlap then the screen appears white.

- When light passes through a filter some of the colours are absorbed so they do not pass through. Filters of the primary colours each allow their own colour to pass through and they absorb the other two primary colours. Filters of the secondary colours allow their own colour to pass through as well as the two primary colours that make up that colour; the other primary colour is absorbed.

- Different objects appear to be different colours when viewed in white light because they act in a similar way to colour filters; they absorb some colours and reflect others. Primary coloured objects reflect light of their own primary colour and absorb the other two. Secondary coloured objects reflect light of their own colour. They also reflect light of the two primary colours that make up the secondary colour. The other primary colour is absorbed.

- Sound travels through the air and other materials by **vibrations of the particles**. The loudness of a sound can be increased by increasing the amplitude of the vibration; the maximum distance the particles move from their normal position. The pitch of a sound is increased by increasing the frequency; this is the number of vibrations that occur each second.

Course Summaries

The Earth and beyond

- The Sun is at the centre of the Solar System. Nine known planets and their moons, along with countless numbers of asteroids, orbit the Sun. The planets in order in the Solar System are: Sun, Mercury, Venus, Mars, (asteroids), Jupiter, Saturn, Uranus, Neptune, Pluto.

- The planets are kept in orbit by the **gravitational** attractive **forces** between each planet and the Sun.

- As the Earth orbits the Sun, our view of the stars changes. The Earth's movement around the Sun is anticlockwise, viewed from a point above the North Pole. This causes the stars to appear to move clockwise around the Earth. The Earth's daily rotation on its axis also causes an apparent clockwise movement of the stars around the Earth.

- The Earth's daily **rotation on its axis** is the cause of night and day. In the northern hemisphere the Sun rises in the east and sets in the west. Days are longer in summer than in winter and the Sun rises higher in the sky in summer. This is due to the Earth's tilt on its axis and results in seasons.

- We see other stars in the sky because they give out light. Some planets and satellites can also be seen clearly in the sky. They are seen by light from the Sun that they reflect. The Moon is the Earth's natural satellite but there are many other (artificial) satellites in orbit around the Earth. Artificial satellites are used to monitor the weather, for communications and surveillance and for navigation. Artificial satellites equipped with telescopes can see much further into the Universe than Earth-based satellites can. Because the light from distant stars takes thousands and millions of years to reach Earth, these satellites are being used to look back in time.

Energy resources and energy transfer

- In Britain most of our electricity is generated using **non-renewable sources**. These are mainly fossil fuels: oil, coal and gas. These fuels cannot be replaced during the lifetime of the Earth. Some of our energy comes from **renewable sources**. All our food relies on plants so it is renewable; wood can be burned and more trees can be grown. The wind can be used to generate electricity, as can waves and the moving water in fast-flowing rivers. A renewable source of energy will not be used up in the Earth's lifetime.

- Most of the energy that we make use of comes from the Sun; the energy contained in plants and fossil fuels was trapped in the process of **photosynthesis**. Wind and waves are caused by the Sun's heating of the Earth and the atmosphere. The exceptions are geothermal energy, which is heat generated by the radioactive decay of rocks below the Earth's surface, and tidal energy, which is mainly due to the Moon's rotation around the Earth.

- Energy is needed to heat objects to a temperature that is warmer than their surroundings and energy is lost to the surroundings when objects cool down.

- An **energy transfer** always takes place when a force causes movement. Raising an object uphill increases its gravitational potential energy; increasing the speed of an object gives it more kinetic energy. Almost all of the energy transferred from electricity and burning fuels ends up as heat; our surroundings, the buildings we inhabit, the ground and the air around us, are warmed by the heat, light and movement that they absorb.

- Energy transfers also take place between objects that are at different temperatures. Energy can be conducted through solids, liquids, and gases. Convection currents only take place in liquids and gases. Liquids can also lose energy through evaporation. All objects radiate energy; this is how energy reaches the Earth from the Sun.

- When an energy transfer takes place, the **total amount of energy always remains the same**. This means that the total energy that flows out of an electrical appliance in the form of heat, light or movement is equal to the total amount of energy that flows in from the electricity supply. However, some of the **energy may be wasted**, for example the heat that flows out of a television set is wasted energy.

- **Energy can be stored** in a number of ways. Plants and fossil fuels store energy from the Sun. Batteries store energy in their chemical make-up and energy from electricity can be stored as gravitational potential energy by pumping water from a low reservoir to a higher one.

Self test - Foundation

Biology

1 a Match up the process names with their meanings. [3]

respiration	getting rid of wastes
excretion	getting food, water, and minerals
movement	adding on new parts
nutrition	releasing energy from food
reproduction	responding to change
sensitivity	change of position
growth	making more of your own kind

b Name one other key feature of living things. [1]

c What is the difference between respiration and breathing? [1]

d People often include fossils in their studies of living things. How would you convince someone that a fossil in a rock had once been alive? [1]

e A virus does not show many features of life. Explain why most people would include it as a living thing. [1]

2 The diagram shows the cell of a plant leaf.

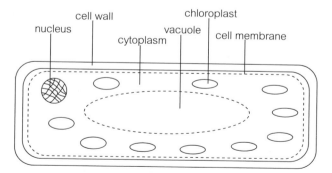

a What two features does this cell have that animal cells do not have? [2]

b What is the main job of the nucleus? [1]

c What job does the cell membrane do? [1]

d What does the chloroplast do? [1]

e State two ways in which the cell shown is adapted for making food. [2]

f Organs form part of systems. Match the organs lists to the systems listed. [2]

liver	circulatory
heart	reproductive
stem	respiratory
leaf	food making
lung	excretory
kidney	digestive
stamen	support

3 a It is possible to group living things by the ways of life they use. These groups are called phyla. Match the phyla with their descriptions. [2]

liver	circulatory
fungi	single celled
plants	have muscles and nerves
animals	green and multicellular
protists	have threads and digest food externally

b Match up the key features listed with the group they belong to. [2]

have a tadpole stage	birds
feathers	mammals
soft shelled eggs	fish
suckle their young on milk	reptiles
fins	amphibians

Self test - Foundation

c Give two reasons why biologists put living things into groups. [2]

d Select the best definition. A species is: [1]

    A a type of organism

    B a group of similar looking organisms

    C a group of successfully interbreeding organisms

    D a group of organisms living in the same area

e Scolecopteris was a fossil plant. It had spores and a transport system. It had a proper stem, root and leaf system. In what group would you classify it? [1]

4 a Match the parts of the reproductive system in plants with what they do. [2]

sepals	makes pollen
stamen	bright to attract insects
ovule	pollen gets caught here
stigma	protects the flower when in bud
petals	attracts insects by scent
nectary	eggs are found here

b Select the best description of pollination. [1]

    A transfer of pollen from stamen to stigma

    B joining of the egg and pollen nucleus

    C blowing pollen on the wind from one flower to another

    D growth of the pollen tube

c Explain how dandelion seeds are dispersed. [1]

d State three changes that happen to girls during puberty. [1]

e State three changes that happen to boys during puberty. [1]

5 a Cats eat thrushes. Snails eat grass. Thrushes eat snails.

    (i) Write a food chain with cats, thrushes, snails, and grass in it. [1]

    (ii) Which organism is the producer? [1]

    (iii) From the organisms above, name a predator and its prey. [1]

b Draw a food web from the food chains given below: [2]

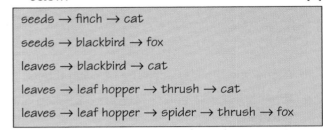

seeds → finch → cat

seeds → blackbird → fox

leaves → blackbird → cat

leaves → leaf hopper → thrush → cat

leaves → leaf hopper → spider → thrush → fox

c Where does all the energy come from that drives a food chain? [1]

d The world is divided into major regions (biomes) based on climate. The most northerly is tundra. Some of the soil is permanently frozen. For half the year the sun barely rises above the horizon.

    (i) What happens to large animals in winter? [1]

    (ii) What sort of plants manage to survive? [1]

    (iii) What will happen to the tundra if global warming occurs? [1]

6 a Match up the dietary needs with what they are used for. [2]

carbohydrates	helps digestion
fats	used for energy
proteins	small amounts prevent disease
vitamins	used for insulation
fibre	used for growth and repair

Self test - Foundation

b Say what we mean by a balanced diet. [1]

c Give two reasons why food we eat needs to be digested? [2]

7 a The graph shows a typical pattern of population growth.

   (i) In which phase is the growth fastest? [1]

   (ii) Give one reason why the growth might level off. [1]

   (iii) what would you expect to happen if at point A the population was given a lot more space? [1]

b A farmer wants to produce a wheat that has short stalks and big ears. His current crop ranges from 0.5 – 1.00 m in height and the ears weigh between 50 and 100 g. How should he go about achieving what he wants? [1]

c Most species produce offspring in large numbers and of different varieties. Explain why this helps the species to survive. [1]

d What is the name of the process that leads to only some varieties surviving. [1]

8 a Complete the word equation for aerobic respiration. [1]

sugar + _____ → energy + _____ + water

b Match the blood vessel type with what it does. [2]

arteries	carry blood towards theheart
capillaries	carry blood away from the heart
lymph vessels	materials exchanged through their walls
veins	collect up liquid from the tissues

c Air is breathed in through the lungs.

   (i) What gas is absorbed? [1]

   (ii) What gas is given out? [1]

   (iii) Where in the lungs does this happen? [1]

   (iv) Why is the windpipe surrounded by rings of cartilage? [1]

   (v) Why are nose and windpipe lined with mucus? [1]

d State two ways the body protects itself from disease. [2]

Chemistry

1 The table gives the melting points and boiling points of four substances and also the number of products formed with the substance burns in oxygen.

substance	melting point in °C	boiling point in °C	products of number of burning
A	113	444	1
B	–117	78	2
C	–182	–162	2
D	122	249	2

a Copy and complete the table showing the state of **A**, **B**, **C**, and **D** at room temperature (20 °C) and atmospheric pressure. [2]

solid	liquid	gas

b On a distant star in the Universe the temperature is 150 °C and the atmospheric conditions are similar to those on the Earth. How would the states of these four substances be different there? [3]

Self test - Foundation

c Why is **A** an element while **B**, **C**, and **D** are either mixtures or compounds? [1]

d Water is a compound of hydrogen and oxygen. Write down **three** differences between water and a mixture of hydrogen and oxygen. [3]

2 The diagram shows the particles in a gas.

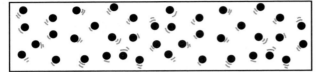

a Describe the movement of these particles. [2]

b Use this model to explain why gases are squashy. [1]

3 Phil has a coloured solution which he believes is a number of coloured dyes dissolved in water.

a (i) Draw a labelled diagram to show how he could get some pure water from this solution. [2]

(ii) Choose the name from the list for the method he is using.

chromatography   distillation
evaporation   fractional distillation   [1]

b Phil wants to show that the liquid he collected is water. How should he test for water and what result would he expect? [2]

c (i) Describe how he would try to show that the solution contains a number of dyes and not just one. [2]

(ii) Choose the name from the list for the method he is using.

chromatography   distillation
evaporation   fractional distillation   [1]

4 Here are four changes involving water:

A hydrogen and oxygen burn to produce water

B liquid water freezes in the deep freezer

C water boils when heated in a kettle

D sugar dissolves in water to form a sugar solution

a In which change does a chemical reaction place? [1]

b A cube of sugar weighing 4 g is dissolved in 100 g of water. What will be the mass of sugar solution formed? [1]

c Two grammes of hydrogen burns in sixteen grammes of oxygen. What mass of water is produced? [1]

5 Sarah heated some lead carbonate in a test tube. She weighed the test tube empty, with lead carbonate, and again after heating.
Here are her results:

mass of empty test tube	= 32.40 g
mass of test tube + lead carbonate	= 35.60 g
mass of test tube and lead carbonate after heating	= 35.07 g

The word equation for the reaction is:

lead carbonate → lead oxide + carbon dioxide

a (i) What mass of lead carbonate did Sarah use? Give the unit. [1]

(ii) Choose the name of this type of reaction from the list.

combustion   oxidation
reduction   thermal decomposition   [1]

(iii) Draw a diagram to show how a test tube filled with carbon dioxide could be collected from the lead carbonate. [2]

b Sarah then heated some copper foil in a Bunsen burner flame. The copper foil went black.

  (i) Write a word equation for the reaction taking place when copper is heated. [1]

  (ii) Would you expect the mass of the copper to increase, decrease, or stay the same when it is heated? Explain your answer. [2]

  (iii) Choose the name of this type of reaction from the list.

    combustion   oxidation

    reduction   thermal decomposition [1]

6 a Copy and complete the table by adding the words from the list.

    igneous   metamorphic   sedimentary [2]

rock sample	description	type of rock
A	Soft rock made up of tiny grains.	
B	Hard rock with sugary appearance	
C	Hard rock made up of large crystals	

b Which rock A, B, or C could have been produced from the cooling of molten rock? [1]

c Which rock A, B, or C would not contain fossils? [1]

d What conditions are needed to turn A into B? [2]

e Explain how C can be turned into A. [3]

7 The table gives the results of testing four solutions with red and blue litmus.

solution	colour of solution when red litmus added	colour of solution when blue litmus added
P	red	red
Q	red	blue
R	blue	blue
S	colourless	colourless

a Which solution could be household bleach? Explain your choice. [2]

b Which solution is shown to be an alkali? [1]

c Which solution is likely to have a pH value of 7? [1]

d Which solution could have a pH value of 4? [1]

e Write down the name of an indicator which shows the pH value of a solution. [1]

f Choose from the list the name of the types of reaction taking place when an acid reacts with an alkali.

    combustion   neutralization

    oxidation   precipitation [1]

g Copy and complete the following general word equation

    acid + alkali → + ... + ... [2]

Self test - Foundation

8 The diagram shows four test tubes. In each test tube a metal is reacting with the same volume of dilute hydrochloric acid at room temperature. In each case there is the same amount of metal in a finely powdered form.

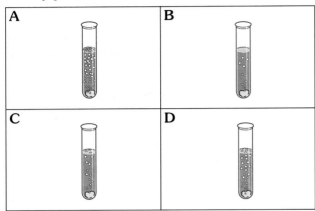

a Arrange the four metals in order of reactivity, putting the most reactive metal first.   [3]

b Write down **three** ways of speeding up the reaction taking place in test tube A.   [3]

c Choose from the list the name of the gas produced in each test tube.

carbon dioxide   hydrogen
nitrogen   oxygen   [1]

9 The metal sodium is kept under paraffin oil so that it does not come into contact with air and water.

a What happens if sodium comes into contact with air?   [2]

b What is produced if it comes into contact with cold water?   [2]

Physics

1 a Which of the following objects are attracted to a magnet?

brass screw
iron nail
plastic spoon
steel spring.   [2]

b Two magnets are placed side-by side on a table so that they are repelling each other.

Draw the magnets and label the other poles.   [2]

2 The diagram shows two lamps and a battery.

a Redraw the diagram using the correct circuit symbols.   [3]

b When the circuit is made, the lamps are dim. How could they be made brighter?   [1]

Lamp A is unscrewed.

c What happens to lamp B?   [1]

d Explain why this happens.   [1]

e Draw a circuit diagram showing how two lamps and two switches can be connected to one battery so that each lamp has its own switch. [2]

3 A helium-filled balloon floats in still air.

a Which arrows show the directions of the two forces that act on the balloon?   [2]

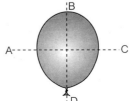

Self test - Foundation

b Write down a statement about the sizes of the two forces when the balloon is not moving. [1]

c Some water is placed in a bucket and the balloon is held under the surface of the water and then released. Explain why the balloon moves up. [1]

4 A glider is being towed by an aircraft.

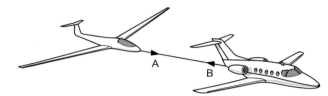

a Write a description of the force labelled A. [2]

b Write a description of the force labelled B. [2]

c What other force acts backwards on the glider? [1]

d What other force acts downwards on the glider? [1]

e The pilot of the aircraft reduces the engine speed. this causes force A to become smaller.

Explain how this affects the speed of the glider. [2]

5 A boy is using the light from a desk lamp to read a book.

a Explain how the boy is able to see the book. [2]

b The pages are white and the printing is black.

(i) Explain why the pages appear white. [1]

(ii) Explain why the printing appears black. [1]

c The boy looks at the book through a green colour filter.

(i) What colour do the pages look to be? [1]

(ii) What colour does the printing look to be? [1]

d The boy is sat 40 cm away from a mirror on the wall. When he looks at the mirror, he sees his image.

(i) Where does his image seem to be?

Choose one option.

A Behind the mirror

B On the mirror

C In front of the mirror [1]

(ii) What is the distance between the boy and his image? [1]

6 In a radio or hi-fi, sound is produced by the paper cone of a loudspeaker.

a How does the paper cone produce a sound? [1]

b How does the sound differ if the frequency of the sound waves is increased? [2]

c Suggest why sound cannot travel in a vacuum. [1]

7 Venus is a planet that can be seen as a bright object in the sky.

a Venus does not give out light. Explain how Venus can be seen in the sky. [2]

Self test - Foundation

b Which option gives the correct description of the position of Venus in the Solar System? [1]

   A Between the Sun and the Earth

   B Between the Earth and Jupiter

   C Beyond Jupiter

c Name one planet that is closer to the Sun than Venus is. [1]

d What is the brightest object that can be seen in the night sky? [1]

8 The diagram shows the Earth's orbit around the Sun.

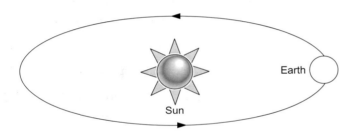

a On a copy of the diagram, shade the part of the Earth that is in darkness. [1]

b Explain what causes night to turn into day on this part of the Earth. [1]

c Draw the position of the Earth six months later than the position shown in the diagram. [1]

d How long does it take for the Earth to return to the position in the diagram? [1]

9 A greenhouse has glass walls that face north, south, east and west.

a Through which wall is the Sun visible at midday in December? [1]

b Through which wall does the Sun shine when it rises in the morning? [1]

c Explain why the Sun shines through the roof of the greenhouse in summer but only through the walls in winter. [1]

10 Oil is a fossil fuel.

a Give the names of two other fossil fuels. [2]

b Where did the energy that is stored in fossil fuels come from? [1]

c Explain why fossil fuels are described as being non renewable. [1]

d Give the name of one renewable source of energy. [1]

11 The diagram shows three positions of a child as she swings on a swing.

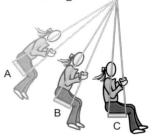

a At which position does she have the most kinetic energy? [1]

b At which position does she have the most potential energy? [1]

c At which position could her kinetic energy be zero? [1]

d The swing slows down and eventually stops. What has happened to the energy that she had while swinging? [1]

12 Energy from electricity can be transferred as heat, movement and light.

Copy and complete the sentences about the energy from a lamp.

a A lamp transfers energy as (a)_____ and _____ . [1]

b The energy transferred as (b)_____ is wasted. [1]

c The energy transferred as (c)_____ is useful. [1]

Self test - Higher

Biology

1 a You have landed on an alien planet. In front of you are three objects. When studying the objects on the planet for life what are the seven signs you will look for. [2]

b If you found a fossil in a rock how would you convince someone that this had once been alive? [1]

c Some people argue that viruses are not alive. What two key features do viruses have that would contradict this? [1]

2 The two cells shown are a liver cell and a nerve cell.

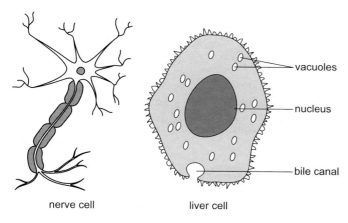

nerve cell   liver cell

a What extra features would you expect a plant cell to have? [1]

b Write down the main function of: the nucleus, the cytoplasm, and the cell membrane? [2]

c State two ways in which the nerve cell is adapted to carry messages. [1]

d Choose a body system for humans from the following list: digestive; skeletal; excretory; reproductive. Name any two organs in the system you have chosen and say what their functions are. [2]

3 a Give two reasons for classifying living things. [1]

b Archaeopteryx is a fossil animal. It has feathers and wings, but probably could not fly.

  (i) What group does it belong to? [1]

  (ii) What sort of eggs would you have expected it to lay? [1]

  (iii) It is a vertebrate animal. What does this mean? [1]

  (iv) Vertebrates are part of a larger phylum of animals which have a central supporting rod. What is the name of this group? [1]

c Write down two features of insects. [1]

4 a What are the two sorts of reproduction? [1]

b Choose the best definition. Fertilization is [1]

  when pollen is carried to the stigma

  when an egg is released from the ovary

  the zygote undergoing its first division

  the egg joining with a sperm

c Why do anthers ripen at a different time from the stigmas? [1]

5 In the human reproductive system:

a Where are sperm made? [1]

b Write down two functions of semen [1]

c Why are the testicles outside the main body cavity? [1]

d How often does an egg get released? [1]

e Approximately how long after menstruation is an egg normally released? [1]

f What is the lining of the womb designed for? [1]

Self test - Higher

6 Oak leaf → caterpillar → thrush → cat.
This is a simple food chain.

  a Name the producer and the top predator. [1]

  b Name one other predator and its prey. [1]

  c Where does the energy come from tha drives the food chain? [1]

  d Why is it likely that there would be fewer cats than thrushes? [1]

  e Imagine this is part of a much bigger food web. In general terms suggest two things that might happen if one year very few caterpillars hatched out. [1]

7 a When DDT (an insecticide) was used in the 1950's it affected animals other than insects. Explain two ways in which DDT affected other animals. [2]

  b Select one organism in a named ecosystem. Explain two ways in which it is adapted to its way of life. [1]

8 Name the food type that gives us most energy. [1]

9 The graph shows the amount of oxygen taken in or given off by a plant over 24 hours.

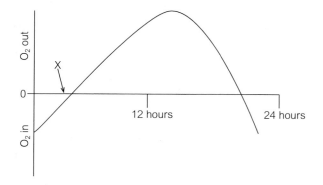

  a Why is oxygen only taken in at night? [1]

  b What is point X on the graph called? [1]

  c What process causes oxygen to be given off? [1]

  d Write the word equation for that process. [1]

10 a If a bacterial cell reproduces every thirty minutes how many will there be after 4 hours starting with one cell? [1]

  b A population of yeast cells is kept in a sealed container. After a day the population starts to decline. Give two reasons why this might happen. [2]

  c What is meant by the carrying capacity of a population? [1]

  d A population of rabbits breeds twice as many young as usual.

    (i) What is likely to happen to the fox population that eats them? [1]

    (ii) What effect will this have on the rabbits? [1]

    (iii) What might have caused the unusual growth of the rabbit population? [1]

  e David and Michael are identical twins.

    (i) Suggest two features they would have in common [1]

    (ii) Explain how we are able to tell them apart. [1]

  f Explain why clean water is one of the main causes of human population growth. [1]

  g A dog breeder has a Labrador family. She wants to produce dogs with shorter legs and shorter hair. How would she go about this? [1]

  h Many bacteria have become resistant to antibiotics. In terms of selection explain how this has happened. [1]

11 a Write a word equation for aerobic respiration. [1]

  b State one difference between the air we breathe in and the air we breathe out. [1]

  c Give two features of the alveoli that help gas exchange to occur. [2]

Self test - Higher

d The heart is a double pump. Why is it helpful to have a double pump? [1]

e Plasma leaks out of the capillaries into tissues. How is it returned to the blood stream? [1]

f Why do veins coming from the legs have valves and those coming from the head not have valves? [1]

12 What are opposing sets of muscles called? [1]

13 Describe three ways in which the body fights disease. [2]

Chemistry

1 The diagram shows the particles in some liquid in an open beaker.

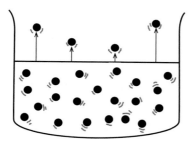

a What happens to the particles in the liquid as the liquid evaporates? [2]

b Why does the liquid cool during the evaporation process? [1]

c Why does the evaporation take place faster at a higher temperature? [2]

d Why does evaporation not take place if the beaker is covered with a lid? [2]

e In some hot countries a small amount of an oil is poured into a water reservoir. Why is this done and how does it work? [3]

2 The diagrams show simple representations of aluminium atoms and iodine atoms in the pure elements.

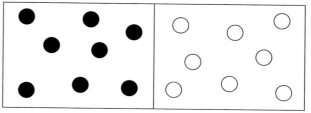

aluminium atoms   *iodine atoms*

a Write down one way in which all aluminium atoms are the same. [1]

b Copy and complete the two diagrams showing a mixture of aluminium and iodine, and the compound aluminium iodide, (AlI_3). [3]

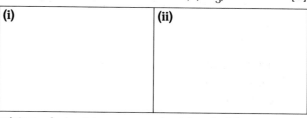

mixture of aluminium and iodine   *aluminium iodide*

3 A compound has a formula $KClO_3$.

a Name the three elements combined in this compound. [2]

b Name the compound. [1]

c When this compound is heated, a compound with the formula KCl is formed and a colourless gas is lost.

   (i) What is the name of the colourless gas lost? [1]

   (ii) What is the name of the compound with the formula KCl? [1]

d Write down the name of a compound containing oxygen, hydrogen, and potassium. [1]

Self test - Higher

4 a Explain how rocks can be weathered by changes in temperature when water is present. [3]

b In the desert, where, there is little water but big changes in temperature between day and night, weathering of rocks still occurs.
Explain processes producing weathering of rocks in desert areas. [4]

5 Coal, oil, and natural gas are three fossil fuels.

a What is meant by the term fossil fuel? [1]

b Name one fuel that is not a fossil fuel. [1]

c The burning of a fuel is an exothermic process. What is meant by the term exothermic? [3]

d What problems are caused by burning fossil fuels? [3]

6 Iron is extracted from iron ore in a blast furnace. The important reaction in the furnace is:

iron(III) oxide + carbon monoxide →
iron + carbon dioxide

a Which of the reactants in the equation is oxidised and which is reduced? Explain your answers. [4]

b What name is given to a reaction where both oxidation and reduction are taking place? [1]

7 Part of the reactivity series is shown below:

magnesium   (most reactive)
zinc
iron
copper   (least reactive)

a Only one of these metals does not react with dilute hydrochloric acid or dilute sulphuric acid. Which metal is this? [1]

b One of these metals is extracted by electrolysis? Which metal is this? [1]

c Sue puts iron filings into magnesium sulphate solution, zinc sulphate solution, and copper(II) sulphate solution in separate test tubes. She finds a reaction takes place in only one test tube.

  (i) In which solution would a reaction take place? [1]

  (ii) Write a word equation for this reaction. [2]

  (iii) Write down three things she would observe during this reaction. [3]

d If a mixture of chromium oxide and aluminium is heated a violent reaction takes place.

  (i) What name is given to this reaction? Choose your answer from this list.

     combustion   *displacement*
     endothermic   *neutralization* [1]

  (ii) Write down a word equation for this reaction. [1]

  (iii) What does this reaction tell us about the positions of aluminium and chromium in the reactivity series? [2]

8 a Sodium sulphate can be prepared by the reaction of sodium hydroxide solution and dilute sulphuric acid.

  (i) Write a word equation for this reaction. [1]

  (ii) What name is given to this reaction? Choose your answer from this list.

     combustion   *displacement*
     endothermic   *neutralisation* [1]

  (iii) How would you attempt to mix the solutions in the correct amounts to produce the pure salt solution? [3]

Self test - Higher

b Copy and complete the following word
equations for reactions producing salts

(i) sodium + chlorine → ....

(ii) sodium carbonate + sodium nitrate →
.... + ... + ...   [3]

Physics

1 A balloon becomes negatively charged when it is
rubbed with a duster. Explain how the balloon
becomes charged.   [2]

2 Some pieces of aluminium foil contain both
positive and negative charges. The diagram shows
how the positive and negative charges are evenly
spread.

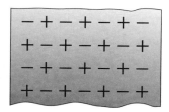

The charged balloon is held near one side of the
aluminium foil.

a Draw a diagram showing the new arrangement
of charge on the foil.   [2]

b Explain why the arrangement of charge changes
when the balloon is held near to the foil.   [1]

c Explain why the foil is attracted to the balloon.
[1]

3 The elctromagnet in a relay consists of a coil of
wire wound on a core.

a Choose the most suitable material for the core
from this list: [1]

brass   copper   iron   steel

b Explain why this is the most suitable material.
Give two reasons.   [2]

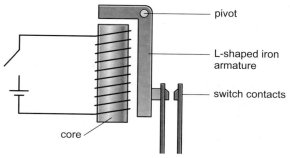

c The diagram shows a relay.

Explain how the switch contacts become
pressed together when the current in the coil is
switched on.   [3]

4 a A cyclist travels a distance of 120 m in a time
of 15 s.Calculate the average speed of the
cyclist.   [3]

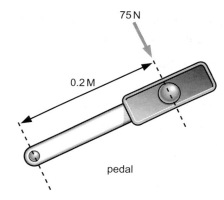

b The diagram shows the push of the cyclist's
foot on the pedal. Calculate the moment
(turning effect) of the force on the pedal.
Give the unit.   [2]

c Write down two ways of increasing the moment
of the force acting on the pedal.   [2]

Self test - Higher

5 A hammer is used to drive a stake into the ground.

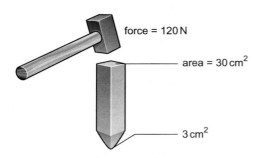

force = 120 N

area = 30 cm²

3 cm²

a Explain why the bottom of the stake is pointed. [2]

b If the force acting on the ground is 120 N, calculate the pressure exerted on the ground. Give the unit. [2]

c A caravan owner places some plastic discs under the legs of the caravan when it is being used on grass. Suggest why she does this. [2]

6 The diagram shows a narrow beam of white light meeting one face of a triangular prism.

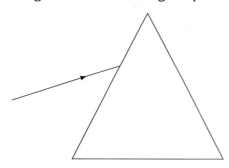

a Draw a diagram to show how the light is dispersed by the prism. Label the colours red and blue. [3]

b A red filter is placed in the path of the beam of white light.

(i) Describe the light that emerges from the prism. [1]

(ii) Explain why this happens. [2]

c (i) What colour does a blue ball appear to be when placed in the path of a beam of red light? [1]

(ii) What colour does a red ball appear to be when placed in the path of a beam of red light?

7 a Copy and complete the diagrams to show how light passes through glass. [3]

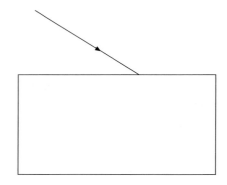

b What is the name of this effect? [1]

8 There are many satellites in orbit around the Earth.

a Which two words in the list describe the force between a satellite and the Earth?

attractive electrostatic gravitational magnetic repulsive [2]

b Give two uses of artificial satellites. [2]

9 On a clear night, the stars appear to move clockwise around the pole star.

a Explain what causes this apparent movement of the stars. [2]

b When viewed at midnight on 1 June, the stars appear to be in a different position to that at midnight on 1 May. Explain what causes this apparent movement of the stars. [2]

Self test - Higher

10 The diagram shows the orbits of the Earth and Jupiter.

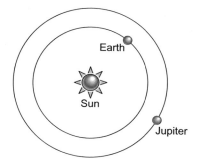

a Which planet's orbit is between those of the Earth and Jupiter? [1]

b The force between Jupiter and the Sun is greater than the force between the Earth and the Sun. Suggest a reason for this. [1]

c A solar-powered satelite is to be placed in orbit around Jupiter. Explain why it needs more solar panels than a similar satellite in orbit around the Earth. [2]

11 A new power station is to be built. It will use fast-growing willow as a fuel.

a Explain why fast-growing willow is a renewable energy source. [1]

b Give one advantage of burning willow instead of coal or gas. [1]

c At night, unwanted electricity from the power station will be stored in water.

Explain how a large mass of water can be used to store unwanted electricity. [2]

d Give one other way in which the energy from electricity can be stored. [1]

12 A car travels at a constant speed up an incline.

a What change is taking place to its

(i) kinetic energy? [1]

(ii) potential energy? [1]

b Energy is needed to move the car up the incline. Where does this energy come from? [1]

13 a A skier speeds up as she travels down a ski run.

What useful energy transfer taking place causes the skier to speed up? [2]

b In a hydroelectric power station, fast-moving water enters the turbines. The water that leaves the turbines is moving slowly. Explain why the water that leaves the turbines is moving slowly. [2]

Self test - Answers

BIOLOGY - FOUNDATION

1a RESPIRATION - releasing energy from food, EXCRETION - getting rid of wastes, MOVEMENT - change of position, NUTRITION - getting food and water and minerals, REPRODUCTION - making more of your own kind, SENSITIVITY - responding to change, GROWTH - adding on new parts (all correct = 3 mk, 4+ = 2 mk, 2/3 = 1 mk); **1b** cells or DNA (or blueprint chemical, or nucleic acid); **1c** breathing is about gas exchange -respiration is releasing energy; **1d** they have the similar forms to present day life - some still have DNA in them - you can show how fossils are formed; **1e** viruses use the same blueprint code as other living things - this implies descent from living things; **2a** cell wall and chloroplast; **2b** control centre; **2c** controls what comes in and out of the cell; **2d** makes food (by photosynthesis); **2e** has many chloroplasts (1), the chloroplasts are near the top of the cell (nearest the light) (1); **2f** LIVER - digestive, HEART - circulatory, STEM - support, LEAF - food making, LUNG - respiratory, KIDNEY - excretory, STAMEN - reproductive (4+ = 2 mk, 1-3 = 1 mk); **3a** FUNGI - have threads and digest food externally, PLANTS - green and multicellular, ANIMALS - have muscles and nerves, PROTISTS - single celled (3/4 = 2 mk, 1/2 = 1 mk); **3b** TADPOLE STAGE - amphibians, FEATHERS - birds, SOFT-SHELLED EGGS - reptiles, SUCKLE THEIR YOUNG ON MILK - mammals, FINS - fish (4+ = 2 mk, 1-3 = 1 mk); **3c** for ease of dealing with large numbers - to show relationships between them; **3d** a species is a group of successfully interbreeding organisms; **3e** a fern; **4a** SEPALS - protects the flower when in bud, STAMEN - makes pollen, OVULE - eggs are found here, STIGMA - pollen gets caught here, PETALS - bright to attract insects, NECTARY - attracts insects by scent (4+ = 2 mk, 1-3 = 1 mk); **4b** A - pollination is transfer of pollen from stamen to stigma; **4c** seed attached to feathery parachute - blown away in the wind; **4d** eggs ripen, hair grows under arms and around genitals, breasts develop, hips broaden, menstruation starts (any 3); **4e** sperm made, hair under arms, around genitals and on face, voice 'breaks', shoulders broaden, muscle strength increases (any 3); **5ai** GRASS → SNAIL → THRUSH → CAT; **5aii** grass; **5aiii** cat/ thrush OR thrush/ snail (either);
5b

seeds →blackbird→fox
leaves→thrush←→cat
→leaf hopper→spider

(complete = 2 mk)
(any 1 = 1 mk)

5c Sun; **5di** they hibernate; **5dii** lichens; **5diii** the ice in the ground will melt and organisms from warmer climates will invade; **6a** CARBOHYDRATES - used for energy, FATS - used for insulation, PROTEINS - used for growth and repair, VITAMINS - small amounts prevent disease, FIBRE - helps digestion (4+ = 2 mk, 1-3 = 1 mk); **6b** everything you need in exactly the right amounts; **6c** to be broken down for absorption (1), and to allow for re-assembly in different ways (1); **7ai** phase A; **7aii** lack of food OR lack of space OR build up of wastes; **7aiii** the population would increase; **7b** he should breed the shortest with the heaviest each generation; **7c** as conditions change some of the varieties will be able to survive the changes; **7d** natural selection; **8a** sugar + OXYGEN → energy + CARBON DIOXIDE + water; **8b** ARTERIES - carry blood away from the heart, CAPILLARIES - materials exchanged through their walls, LYMPH VESSELS - collect up liquid from the tissues, VEINS - carry blood towards the heart (3/4 = 2 mk, 1/2 = 1 mk; **8ci** oxygen; **8cii** carbon dioxide; **8ciii** the alveoli; **8civ** hold it open; **8cv** a dirt and dust trap; **8d** stomach acid, white blood cells, interferon, skin oil, mucus in the respiratory passages, ear wax, tears (any 2)

CHEMISTRY - FOUNDATION

1a solid-A/D, liquid-B, gas-C (all correct = 2 mk; 2/3 correct = 1 mk); **1b** A-liquid, B-gas, C-liquid; **1c** A forms only a single product on burning; **1d** water is a liquid/ hydrogen and oxygen are (1), water has a fixed composition (1), water does not burn/ mixture does (1); **2a** rapid (1), in all directions/ random (1); **2b** there is a lot of space between the particles (1); **3ai** drawing of distillation apparatus (2) (deduct 1 for any slight mistake); **3aii** distillation (1); **3b** boil the liquid (1), boils at 100 °C (1) OR add anhydrous copper sulphate (1), turns blue (1) OR add cobalt chloride paper (1), turns pink (1); **3ci** make a spot on a filter paper and enlarge it with drops of water (1), one ring formed for each dye present (1); **3cii** chromatography; **4a** A; **4b** 104 g; **4c** 18 g; **5ai** 3.20g; **5aii** thermal decomposition; **5aiii** (see text) (allow 1 mark for a slight mistake); **5bi** copper + oxygen → copper oxide; **5bii** increase (1), copper takes in oxygen from the air (1); **5biii** oxidation; **6a** A-sedimentary, B-metamorphic, C-igneous (all correct = 2 mk, 2 correct = 1 mk); **6b** igneous; **6c** C; **6d** high temperature (1), high pressure (1); **6e** weathering and erosion of rock (1), forms sediments (1), sediments washed into lake or sea (1), sediments compressed (1), sediments cemented (1) (any three points for max 3 mk); **7a** S (1), removes colour from the indicator (1); **7b** R; **7c** Q; **7d** P; **7e** Universal indicator; **7f** neutralization; **7g** salt (1) + water (1); **8a** ADCB (3) (A before D (1), D before C (1), C before B (1)); **8b** heat the test tube (1), use more concentrated acid (1), powder the metal (1); **8c** hydrogen; **9a** sodium reacts with oxygen (1), forms sodium oxide (1); **9b** sodium hydroxide (1), hydrogen (1)

PHYSICS - FOUNDATION

1a iron nail, steel spring; **1b** S pole shown at bottom of left hand magnet N pole at top and S pole at bottom of right hand magnet; **2a** correct symbol for cell correct symbol for lamp, circuit shows one cell and two lamps in series; **2b** by using another cell in series with the one shown; **2c** it goes off; **2d** there is no longer a complete circuit; **2e** diagram shows two lamps in parallel - there is a switch in each branch of the circuit; **3a** B and D; **3b** the forces are equal in size; **3c** the upward force is greater than the downward force; **4a** the pull of the rope on the glider; **4b** the pull of the rope on the aircraft; **4c** air resistance; **4d** the Earth's pull or the weight; **4e** the glider slows down because the backwards force is greater than the forwards force; **5a** light from the lamp is reflected by the book; **5bi** the pages reflect all the light from the lamp; **5bii** the printing absorbs all the light from the lamp; **5ci** green; **5cii** black; **5di** A; **5dii** 80 cm; **6a** It vibrates; **6b** pitch increases; **6c** there are no particles to vibrate; **7a** light from the Sun is reflected by Venus; **7b** A; **7c** Mercury; **7d** the Moon; **8a** the diagram shows the part of the Earth facing away from the Sun shaded; **8b** the Earth's rotation; **8c** the position is diametrically opposite to that shown; **8d** 1 year; **9a** South; **9b** East; **9c** the Sun is higher in the sky in summer; **10a** coal, gas; **10b** the Sun; **10c** no more of them can be made in the Earth's lifetime; **10d** any one renewable source; eg wind, waves, tides, hydroelectric, wood; **11a** C; **11b** A; **11c** A; **11d** it has been transferred to heat; **12a** heat, light (either order); **12b** heat; **12c** light.

BIOLOGY - HIGHER

1a respiration, excretion, movement, nutrition, reproduction, sensitivity, growth (5+ = 2 mk, 1-4 = 1 mk); **1b** they have the similar forms to present day life - some still have DNA in them - you can show how fossils are formed (any 2); **1c** they reproduce and have DNA (RNA);

Self test - Answers

2a chloroplasts and cell wall; **2b** nucleus is control centre, cytoplasm is where things are made, cell membrane controls entry and exit (all 3 = 2 mk, else 1); **2c** long thin transfer section, many input lines; **2d** (see text, 2 points for two organ/ function pairs, one for one); **3a** for ease of dealing with large numbers - to show relationships between them; **3bi** birds; **3bii** hard shelled and yolky; **3biii** it has bones; **3biv** chordates; **3c** six legs, three body regions, wings, compound eyes (any 2); **4a** asexual and sexual; **4b** fertilisation is the egg joining with a sperm; **4c** to prevent self-fertilization; **5a** in the testes; **5b** feed and protect sperm; **5c** to keep them cool; **5d** once a month; **5e** two weeks; **5f** feeding the baby; **6a** oak leaf and cat; **6b** cat and thrush OR thrush and caterpillar; **6c** the Sun; **6d** less energy gets to the top of the food chain; **6e** the producers would grow better - the predators would need to find other prey or would suffer; **7a** it builds up as a poison inside and kills - it affects egg shell production in birds; **7b** (see text - mark only for each correctly explained adaptation); **8** carbohydrates; **9a** because there is no photosynthesis in the dark OR only respiration occurs at night; **9b** compensation point; **9c** photosynthesis; **9d** carbon dioxide + water (with sunlight and chlorophyll) → sugar + oxygen; **10a** 256; **10b** lack of food - excess waste accumulation - overcrowding (any 2); **10c** the total number of a population that a particular set of conditions can sustain; **10di** foxes produce more young; **10dii** reduce the numbers; **10diii** extra food, good weather, lower predation; **10ei** (any two genetically determined traits); **10eii** because environmental changes will be different for both; **10f** it breaks the link with reinfection by harmful diseases; **10g** breed together the shortest legged animals with the shortest haired animals each generation; **10h** bacteria have a wide variety of types - some may accidentally be resistant - they will survive and so breed more in the next generation; **11a** SUGAR + OXYGEN → ENERGY + CARBON DIOXIDE + WATER; **11b** breathed in - less carbon dioxide/ more oxygen/ drier/ cooler, breathed out - less oxygen/ more carbon dioxide/ damper/ warmer; **11c** thin walls OR good blood supply OR damp (any 2 for 1 mark each); **11d** it speeds up the flow of oxygenated blood/makes transport of oxygen more efficient; **11e** in lymph vessels; **11f** gravity; **12** antagonistic; **13** antibodies, interferon, various secretions

CHEMISTRY - HIGHER

1a particles escape from liquid into space above (1), high energy (or fast moving particles) escape (1); **1b** lower energy particles are left; **1c** particles have higher (average) energy (1), more can escape from the liquid (1); **1d** water particles in the space cannot escape (1), these particles return to the liquid (1); **1e** oil floats on water (1), large oil particles do no escape so oil does not evaporate (1), oil prevents water particles escaping from the liquid (1); **2a** same number of protons (also same number of electrons) (1); **2b** mixture - aluminium and iodine atoms mixed but not combined (1), compound - aluminium and iodine atoms combined (1), one aluminium atom to three iodine atoms (1); **3a** potassium, chlorine, oxygen, (all three = 2 mk, 2 correct = 1 mk (1); **3b** potassium chlorate; **3ci** oxygen; **3cii** potassium chloride; **3d** potassium hydroxide; **4a** water enters cracks in the rock (1), when very cold water freezes and expands (1), ice thaws and rock breaks up (1), process repeated over and over again (1) (second point must be made plus two others for three marks); **4b** when heated rocks expand and cooled contract (1), these changes put internal pressures on rock (1), wind blows sand (1), erosion caused by sand (sand-blasting) (1); **5a** a substance which burns to release energy and was made from the decomposition of organic material over millions of years; **5b** eg wood, paper; **5c** energy given out; **5d** produce carbon dioxide (1), increase CO2 levels in the atmosphere (1), increase global warming (1), one effect of global warming e.g. rise in temperature, melting of ice caps, rise in sea level (1) (any three points); **6a** iron(III) oxide reduced (1), oxygen is removed (1), carbon monoxide oxidized (1), oxygen is added (1); **6b** redox reaction; **7a** copper; **7b** magnesium; **7ci** test tube containing copper(II) sulphate solution; **7cii** copper(II) sulphate + iron → iron(II) sulphate + copper (2) (one mark for LHS, one mark for RHS); **7ciii** brown metal formed (1), blue solution goes colourless (or fades) (1), solution feels warm (1); **7di** displacement; **7dii** chromium oxide + aluminium → chromium + aluminium oxide; **7diii** aluminium is above chromium in the reactivity series (2) (allow one mark for aluminium is high or chromium is low); **8ai** sodium hydroxide + sulphuric acid → sodium sulphate + water; **8aii** neutralization; **8aiii** measure out volume of sodium hydroxide solution and add indicator (1), add sulphuric acid until neutral (1), repeat with fresh sample of sodium hydroxide solution adding the same volume of acid (1); **8bi** sodium + chlorine → sodium chloride; **8bii** sodium carbonate + nitric acid → sodium nitrate + carbon dioxide + water (3)(3 mk for 4 correct, 2 mk for 3 correct, 1 mk for 1 or 2 correct)

PHYSICS - HIGHER

1a friction between the balloon and the duster causes charges to move from one to the other; **2a** diagram shows excess positive charge on the part of the foil near the balloon and excess negative charge on the part of the foil away from the balloon; **2b** negative charges are repelled by the balloon; **2c** there is an attractive force between the positive charges and the balloon; **3a** iron; **3b** iron magnetizes easily/ iron loses its magnetism easily; **3c** any three points from: the coil has a magnetic field/ the iron core is magnetized/ the armature is attracted to the core/ the armature turns about the pivot; **4a** speed = distance ÷ time = 120 m ÷ 15 s = 0.8 m/s; **4b** moment = force x shortest distance to pivot = 75 N x 0.2 m = 15 Nm; **4c** use a greater force/ move the force further from the pivot; **5a** the point has a small area so the skate exerts a large pressure on the ground; **5b** pressure = force ÷ area = 120 N ÷ 3 cm² = 40 N/cm² ; **5c** to make the weight of the caravan act over a large area - his reduces the pressure on the ground and prevents the caravan sinking; **6a** diagram shows; dispersion at the first face/ dispersion at the second face/ change in direction of blue light greater than that of red light; **6bi** red light; **6bii** a red filter absorbs blue light and green light; **6ci** black; **6cii** red; **7a** left hand diagram: correct change in direction as light enters the block correct change in direction as light leaves the block right hand diagram: light passes through the block undeviated (see text); **7b** refraction; **8a** attractive/gravitational; **8b** any two from: monitoring the weather / communications/ surveillance/ navigation/ astronomy; **9a** the Earth's rotation on its axis; **9b** the Earth's movement around the Sun; **10a** Mars; **10b** Jupiter has more mass; **10c** Jupiter is further from the Sun so the radiation from the Sun is more spread out; **11a** new wood can be grown to replace the wood that is burned; **11b** It does not use up fossil fuels; **11c** the water is pumped from a low reservoir to a higher one - the energy is stored as gravitational potential energy; **11d** In a battery OR in a storage heater/ hot water tank; **12ai** None; **12aii** increases; **12b** from the fuel; **13a** from gravitational potential energy to kinetic energy; **13b** energy is needed to turn the turbines/generate electricity - this energy comes from the kinetic energy of the water.

NOTE: each test is 180 marks (60 / section).

Index